PHILIP'S BRITAIN & IRELAND

2018 STARGAZING

MONTH-BY-MONTH GUIDE TO THE NIGHT SKY

HEATHER COUPER & NIGEL HENBEST

www.philipsastronomy.com
www.philips-maps.co.uk

Published in Great Britain in 2017 by Philip's,
a division of Octopus Publishing Group Limited
(www.octopusbooks.co.uk)
Carmelite House, 50 Victoria Embankment,
London EC4Y 0DZ
An Hachette UK Company (www.hachette.co.uk)

ISBN 978-1-84907-464-3

A CIP catalogue record for this book is available from the British Library.

Printed in China

Welcome to the magical world of stargazing! Within these pages, you'll find your complete guide to everything that's happening in the night sky throughout 2018 – whether you're a beginner or a seasoned astronomer.

With the 12 monthly star charts, you can find your way around the sky on any night in the year. Impress your friends by identifying celestial sights ranging from the brightest planets to some pretty obscure constellations: plus, this year, a couple of comets thrown in for good measure!

Our redesigned compact and colourful *Stargazing 2018* is bang up to date, with extra pages so that you're completely in the picture about everything that's new this year, from shooting stars to eclipses.

THE MONTHLY CHARTS

A reliable map is just as essential for exploring the heavens as it is for visiting a foreign country. For each month, we provide a circular **star chart** showing the whole evening sky, with the horizon around the edge and the overhead point (the zenith) in the centre. To keep the maps uncluttered, we've plotted about 200 of the brighter stars, which means you can pick out the main star patterns – the constellations. (If we'd shown every star visible on a really dark night, there'd be around 3000 stars on the charts!) We also show the ecliptic: the apparent path of the Sun in the sky, which is closely followed by the Moon and planets as well.

You can use these charts throughout the UK and Ireland, along with most of Europe, North America and northern Asia – between 40 and 60 degrees north – though our detailed timings apply specifically to the UK and Ireland.

USING THE STAR CHARTS

Start by finding your compass points. South is where the Sun is highest in the sky during the day; east is roughly where the Sun rises, and west where it sets. At night, you can find north by locating the Pole Star – Polaris – by using the stars of the Plough (see December).

The left-hand chart then shows your view to the north. Most of the stars here are visible all year: these circumpolar constellations wheel around Polaris as the seasons progress.

Your view to the south appears in the right-hand chart; it changes much more as the Earth orbits the Sun. Leo's prominent 'sickle' is high in the spring skies. Summer is dominated by the bright trio of Vega, Deneb and Altair. Autumn's familiar marker is the Square of Pegasus, while the stars of Orion rule the winter sky.

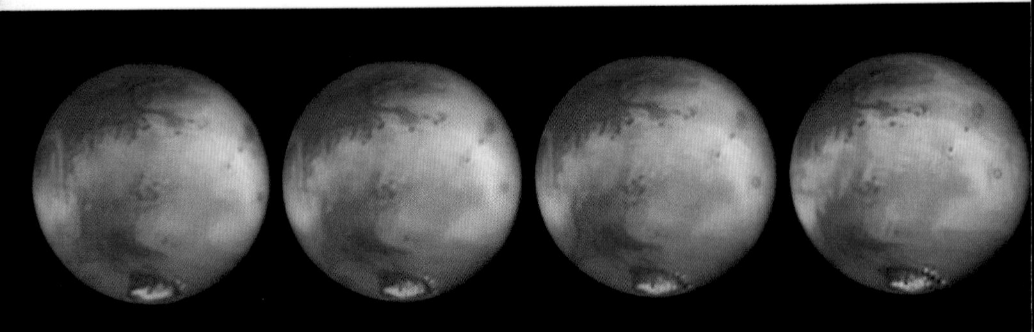

During the night, our perspective on the sky also alters as the Earth spins around, making the stars and planets appear to rise in the east and set in the west. The charts depict the sky in the late evening (the exact times are noted in the captions). As a rule of thumb, if you are observing 2 hours later, then the following month's map will be a better guide to the stars on view – though beware: the Moon and planets won't be in the right place!

THE PLANETS, MOON AND SPECIAL EVENTS

Our charts also highlight the **planets** above the horizon in the late evening. We've indicated the track of any **comets** known at the time of writing, though we're afraid we can't guide you to a comet that's found after the book has been printed!

We've plotted the position of the Full Moon each month, and also the **Moon's position** at three-day intervals before and afterwards. If there's a **meteor shower** in the month, we mark its radiant – the position from which the meteors stream.

The **Calendar** provides a daily guide to the Moon's phases and other celestial happenings. The most interesting are detailed in the **Special Events** section, including close pairings of planets, times of equinoxes and solstices and – most exciting – **eclipses** of the Moon and Sun.

Check out the **Planet Watch** page for more about the other worlds of the Solar System, showing what they're up to when they're not on the main monthly charts. We've illustrated unusual planetary, lunar and cometary goings-on in the new **Planet Event Charts**.

Opposite: Mars captured on 12 April 2014 by Damian Peach (see page 45).

There's a full annual overview of events in the **Solar System Almanac** on pages 78–81. Here we also unravel some puzzling astronomical terms: how brightnesses are measured in *magnitudes*, distances in *light years* and separations in *degrees*.

MONTHLY OBJECTS, TOPICS AND PICTURES

Each month, we examine one particularly interesting **object**: a planet, perhaps, or a star or a galaxy. We also feature a spectacular **picture** – taken by a backyard amateur from Britain – and describe how the image was captured. And we explore a fascinating and often newsworthy **topic**, ranging from supernovae to the Search for Extra-terrestrial Intelligence.

GETTING IN DEEPER

There's a practical **observing tip** each month, helping you to explore the sky with the naked eye, binoculars or a telescope. If you're after 'faint fuzzies' too dim to appear on the charts, we've provided a constellation-by-constellation list (pages 82–85) of recommended **deep-sky objects**, such as nebulae, star clusters and galaxies.

For a round-up of what's new in **observing technology**, go to pages 86–89, where equipment expert Robin Scagell offers advice on how to choose binoculars and telescopes. And – new this year – your darkest places to spot the stars in Great Britain. With these **dark-sky maps**, you can find out where to catch the most breathtaking views of the heavens (pages 92–95).

So: fingers crossed for good weather, glorious eclipses, a multitude of meteors and – the occasional surprise.

Happy stargazing!

- The sky at 10 pm in mid-January, with Moon positions at three-day intervals either side of Full Moon.
- The star positions are also correct for 11 pm at the beginning of January, and 9 pm at the end of the month.
- The planets move slightly relative to the stars during the month.

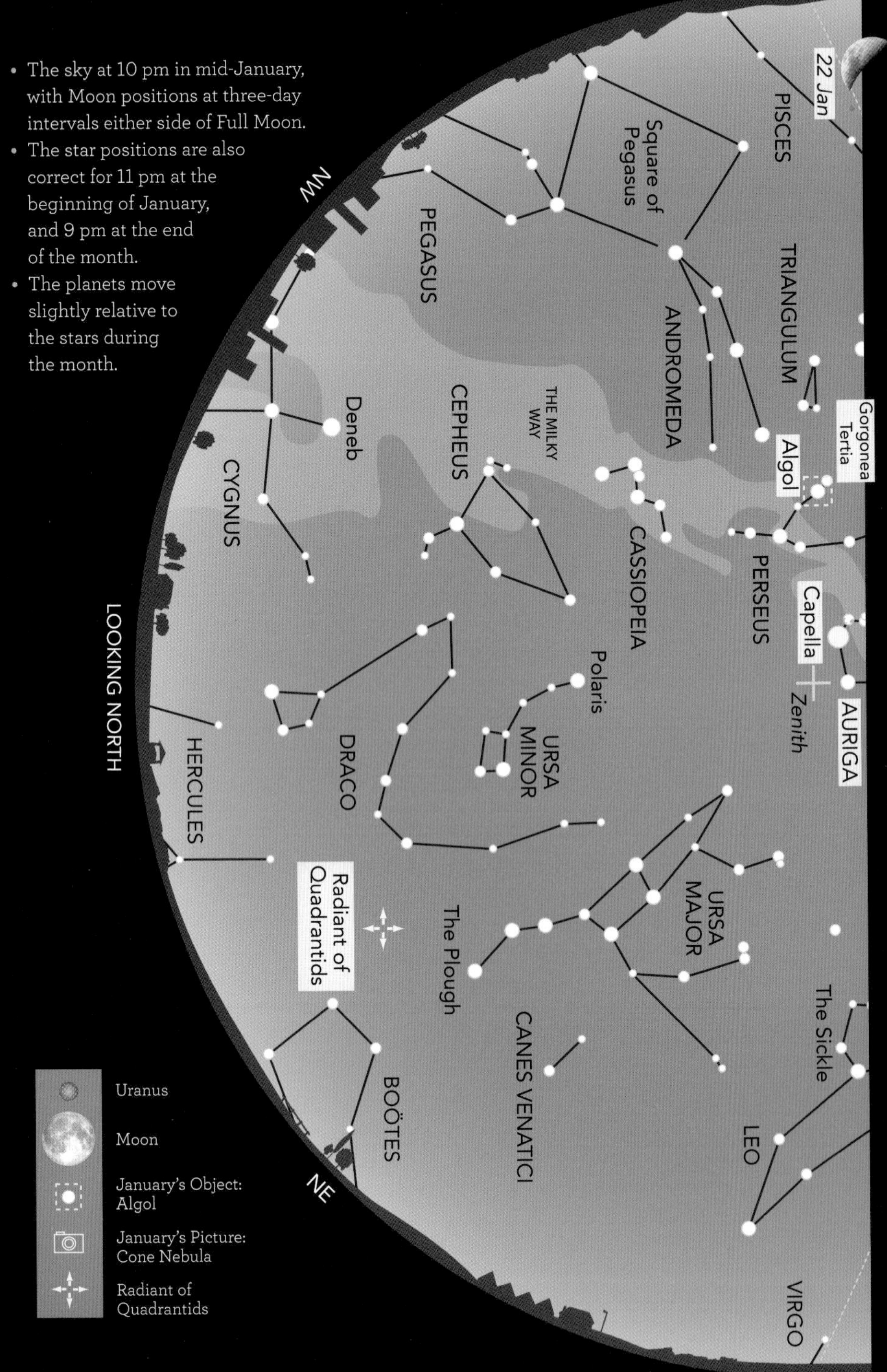

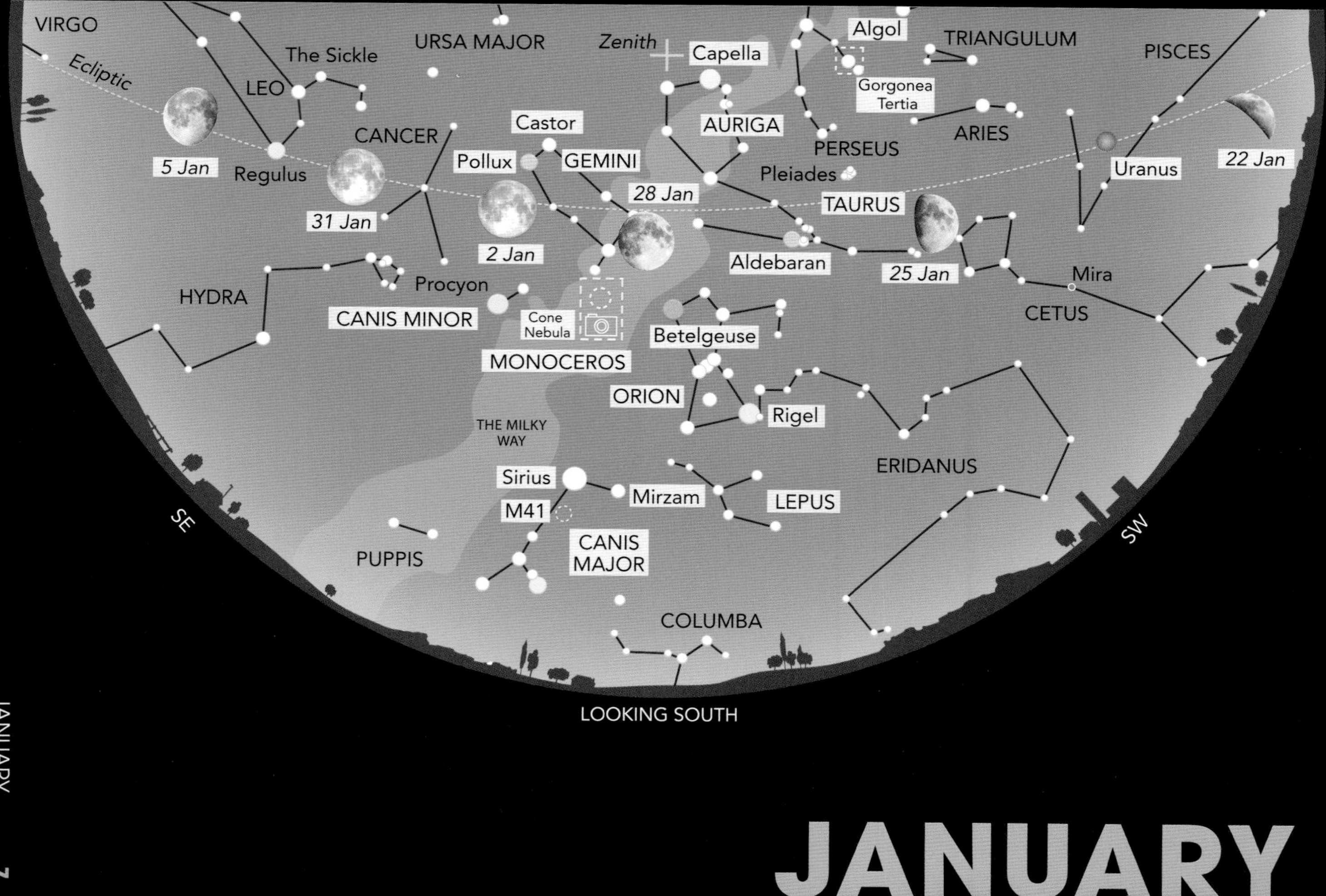
EAST
WEST
SE
SW
LOOKING SOUTH
VIRGO
Ecliptic
URSA MAJOR
The Sickle
LEO
Zenith
Capella
Algol
TRIANGULUM
PISCES
Gorgonea Tertia
ARIES
CANCER
Castor
AURIGA
PERSEUS
5 Jan
Regulus
Pollux
GEMINI
Pleiades
Uranus
22 Jan
28 Jan
TAURUS
31 Jan
2 Jan
Aldebaran
25 Jan
Procyon
Mira
HYDRA
CANIS MINOR
Cone Nebula
CETUS
Betelgeuse
MONOCEROS
ORION
Rigel
THE MILKY WAY
ERIDANUS
Sirius
Mirzam
LEPUS
M41
CANIS MAJOR
PUPPIS
COLUMBA
JANUARY

JANUARY

The year kicks off with a dazzling supermoon, accompanied by a chorus line of brilliant stars, led by **Betelgeuse** and **Rigel** in the magnificent hunter **Orion**. Nearby, you'll find **Aldebaran**, the bright red eye of **Taurus** (the Bull); **Capella**, adorning **Auriga** (the Charioteer); **Castor** and **Pollux**, the celestial twins in **Gemini** and glorious **Sirius**, in **Canis Major** (the Great Dog). If you're a lark, you can also enjoy watching four planets waltzing in the pre-dawn sky, enjoying a couple of *very* close encounters.

JANUARY'S CONSTELLATION

Crowned by **Sirius**, the brightest star in the sky, **Canis Major** is the larger of Orion's two hunting dogs. He is represented as chasing **Lepus** (the Hare), a very faint constellation below Orion, but his main quarry is **Taurus** – take a line from Sirius through Orion's Belt, and you'll spot the celestial bovine on the other side. Arabian astronomers accorded great importance to Canis Major, while the Indians regarded both cosmic dogs (**Canis Minor** lies to the left of Orion) as being 'watchdogs of the Milky Way', which runs between the two constellations.

To the right of Sirius is the star **Mirzam**. Its Arabic name means 'the announcer', because the presence of Mirzam heralded the appearance of Sirius, one of the heaven's most venerated stars. Just below Sirius is the beautiful star cluster, **M41**. This lovely grouping of around a hundred young stars – 2300 light years away – is easily visible through binoculars, and even to the unaided eye. It's rumoured that the Greek philosopher Aristotle, in 325 BC, called it 'a cloudy spot' – the earliest description of a deep-sky object.

OBSERVING TIP

If you want to stargaze at this most glorious time of year, dress up warmly. Lots of layers are better than just a heavy coat, as they trap more air close to your skin, while heavy-soled boots with two pairs of socks stop the frost creeping up your legs. It may sound anorak-ish, but a woolly hat prevents a lot of your body heat escaping through the top of your head. And – alas – no hipflask of whisky. Alcohol constricts the veins, making you feel even colder.

JANUARY'S OBJECT

The star **Algol**, in the constellation **Perseus**, represents the head of the dreadful Gorgon Medusa. In Arabic, its name means 'the demon'. Watch Algol carefully and you'll see why. Every 2 days 21 hours, Algol dims in brightness for several hours, to become as faint as the star lying to its lower right (**Gorgonea Tertia**).

In 1783, an 18-year-old profoundly deaf amateur astronomer from York, John Goodricke, discovered Algol's regular changes, and proposed that the star was orbited by a large dark planet that periodically blocks off some of its light. We now know that Algol does indeed have a dim companion blocking its brilliant light, but it's a fainter star, rather than a planet.

British expatriate Sara Wager of Olocau near Valencia, Spain, obtained this image of the Cone Nebula with a cooled CCD on an AstroTech 300mm Ritchey-Chrétien reflector with two Astrodon narrowband filters. She took 25 exposures of light from hydrogen and 18 of sulphur emissions, each half an hour long - an amazing total of over 21 hours!

JANUARY'S TOPIC: OF SUPERMOONS AND BLUE MOONS

We're treated to a particularly big and bright Full Moon to open the year. On the night of **1/2 January**, our companion world is at its closest point in 2018 – just 356,567 kilometres away – and appears 14 per cent bigger than when the Moon is furthest away. By coincidence the Moon is Full the same night, so the brilliant orb will be extra bright – some 30 per cent more luminous than the faintest Full Moon.

A Full Moon at the closest point in its orbit (perigee) is called a 'supermoon'. This catchy phrase wasn't invented by astronomers, but by astrologers who've tried to link supermoons with earthquakes, tsunamis or volcanic eruptions. But the supermoon's extra gravitational pull is actually only 3 per cent more powerful than average – so we can confidently predict it will cause no natural calamities!

At the end of the month, we have a 'blue moon' – the second Full Moon in a single month. That's not a phrase with any scientific history either, but derives from American farming almanacs. The 'blue moon' on **31 January** suffers a lunar eclipse; because some of the Sun's reddish light is bent round into the Earth's shadow, it will actually appear red.

JANUARY'S PICTURE

This spooky, looming cloud of gas and dust is part of a giant star-forming region in the constellation **Monoceros**. The **Cone Nebula** was discovered in 1785 by William Herschel. Today, we know that the nebula lies 2700 light years away, and is a staggering seven light years long. Its weird shape consists of cosmic dust sculpted by the radiation of nearby stars; this dark material is poised to create new stars and planets in the future.

JANUARY'S CALENDAR

SUNDAY	MONDAY	TUESDAY	WEDNESDAY	THURSDAY	FRIDAY	SATURDAY
	1 Mercury greatest western elongation (am); 9.54 pm Moon close perigee	2 2.24 am Full Moon; supermoon	3 5.35 am Earth at perihelion; Quadrantid meteor shower	4 Quadrantid meteor shower (am); Moon near Regulus	5	6
7 Close conjunction of Mars and Jupiter (am; see Planet Watch)	8 10.25 pm Last Quarter Moon	9 Moon near Spica	10	11 Moon near Jupiter and Mars (am)	12	13 Close conjunction of Mercury and Saturn (am; see Planet Watch)
14	15 Moon near Mercury and Saturn (am)	16	17 2.17 am New Moon	18	19	20 Moon near Neptune
21	22	23	24 10.20 pm First Quarter Moon	25	26	27 Moon near Aldebaran
28	29	30	31 1.27 pm Full Moon; 'blue moon'; total lunar eclipse			

SPECIAL EVENTS

- **Night of 1/2 January:** the Moon is at its closest to the Earth this year, making the Full Moon appear as an exceptionally large and bright 'supermoon' (see this month's Topic).
- **3 January:** the Earth reaches perihelion, its nearest to the Sun at 147 million km.
- **Night of 3/4 January:** tiny particles of dust from the old comet 2003 EH_1 burn up in Earth's atmosphere, as the **Quadrantid** meteor shower. This year, bright moonlight spoils the show.
- **11, 15 January:** the Moon passes Jupiter, Mercury and Saturn in the morning sky (Chart 1b).
- **31 January:** a total lunar eclipse is visible from North America and Asia (but not from the UK) as the Full Moon moves entirely into the Earth's shadow. As the second Full Moon of the month, it's sometimes called a 'blue moon' (see this month's Topic).

JANUARY'S PLANET WATCH

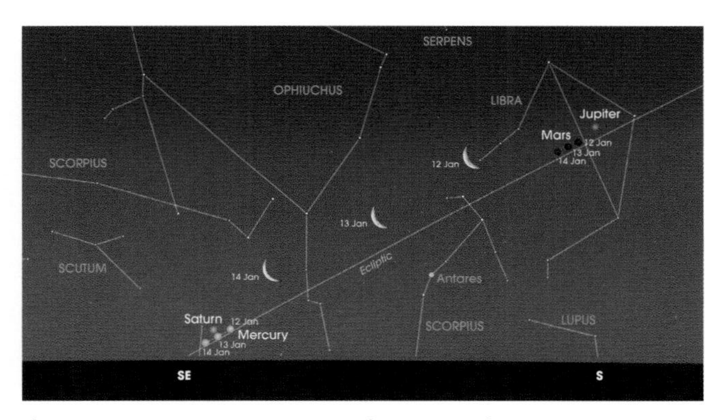

1a *3–11 January, 6.15 am. Conjunction of Mars and Jupiter.*

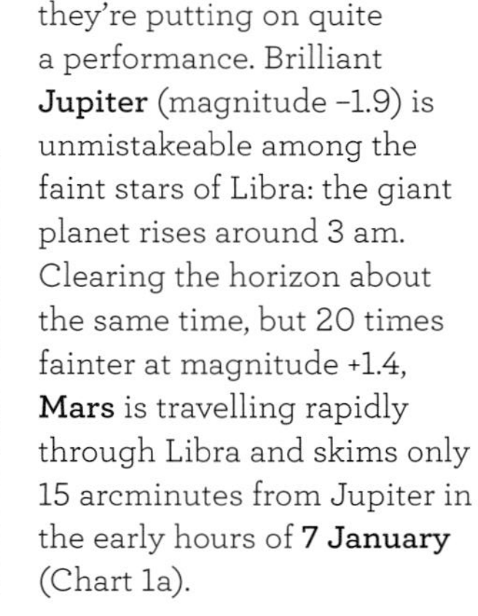

1b *12–14 January, 7 am. Conjunction of Mercury and Saturn.*

• You'll have to be up before dawn to catch any naked-eye planets this month – and they're putting on quite a performance. Brilliant **Jupiter** (magnitude –1.9) is unmistakeable among the faint stars of Libra: the giant planet rises around 3 am. Clearing the horizon about the same time, but 20 times fainter at magnitude +1.4, **Mars** is travelling rapidly through Libra and skims only 15 arcminutes from Jupiter in the early hours of **7 January** (Chart 1a).

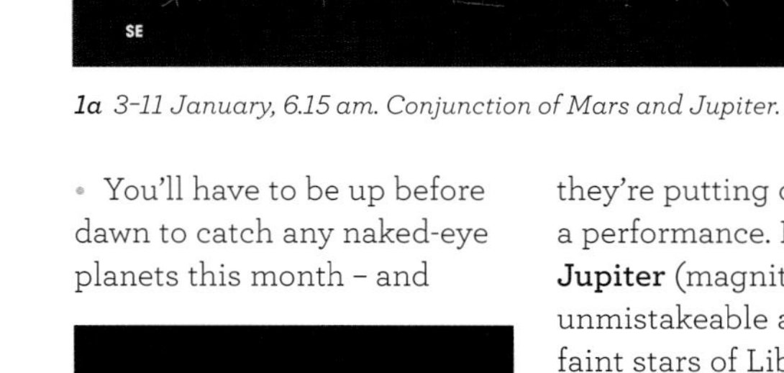

Jupiter

• At the start of the year, you can catch **Mercury** very low in the south-east just before dawn, shining at magnitude –0.3. As this tiny world drops down into the twilight, it speeds past **Saturn** (at magnitude +0.5, only half Mercury's brightness) on the morning of **13 January** at only 40 arcminutes' distance (Chart 1b). In the latter half of the month, Saturn is left on its own, rising about 6.30 am in Sagittarius.

• The evening sky is home to the two most remote planets. Dim **Neptune** (magnitude +7.9) inhabits Aquarius, and sets around 8.30 pm. Slightly brighter **Uranus** lies in Pisces; on the borderline of naked eye visibility at magnitude +5.8, it sets about 0.30 am.

• **Venus** is too close to the Sun to be seen this month.

- The sky at 10 pm in mid-February, with Moon positions at three-day intervals either side of Full Moon.
- The star positions are also correct for 11 pm at the beginning of February, and 9 pm at the end of the month.
- The planets move slightly relative to the stars during the month.

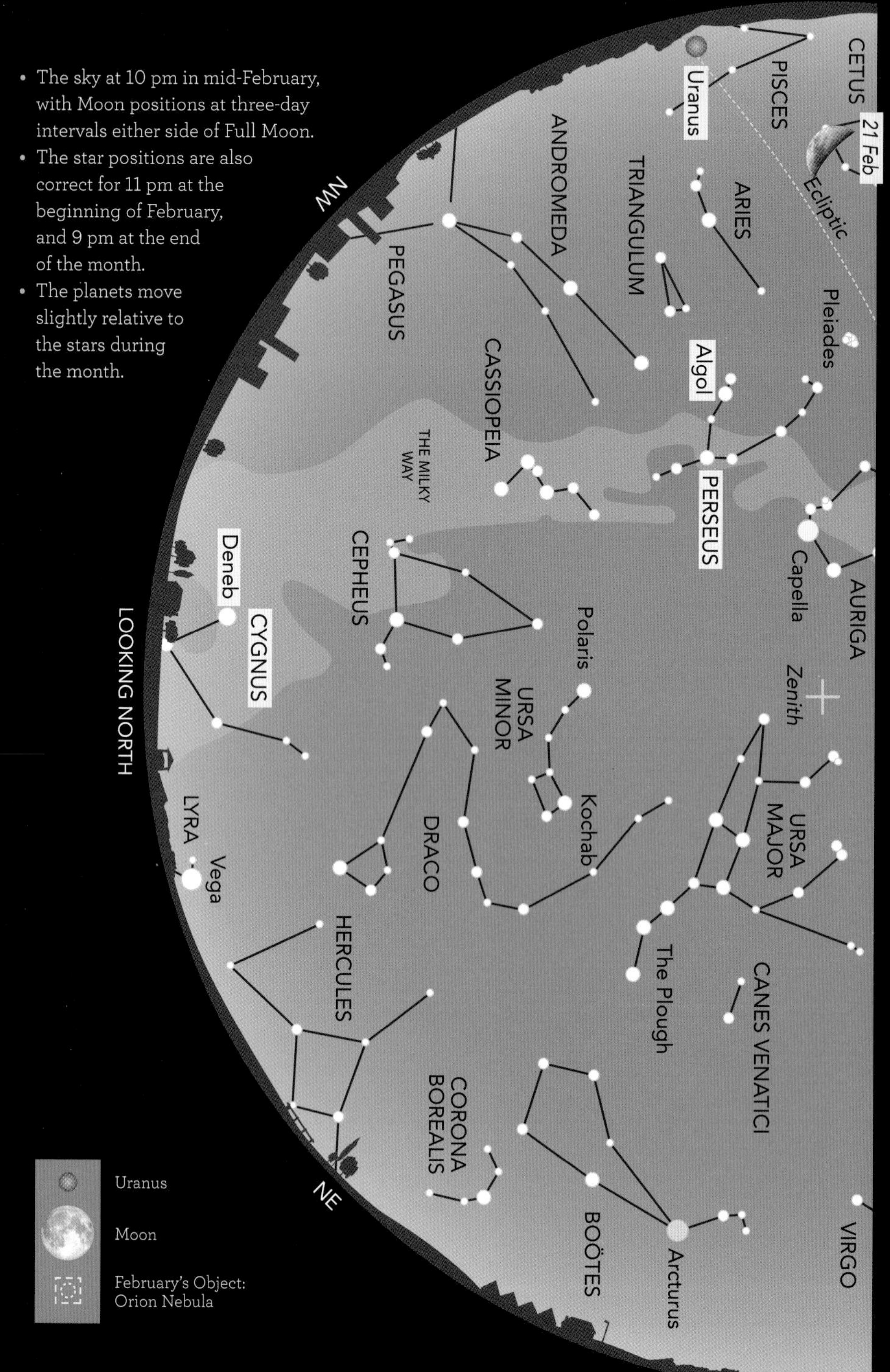

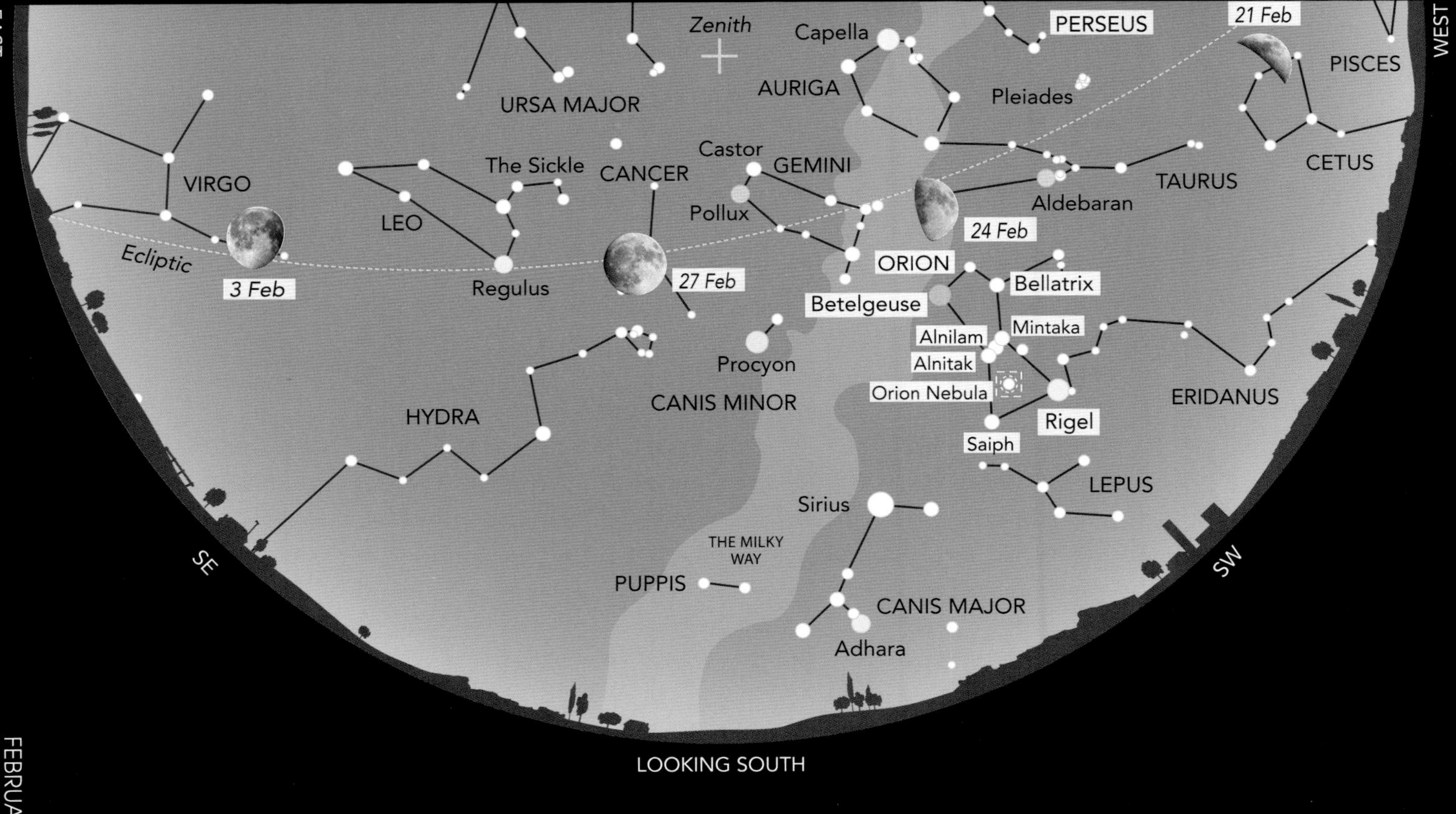
EAST
WEST
Zenith
Capella
PERSEUS
21 Feb
PISCES
URSA MAJOR
AURIGA
Pleiades
CETUS
Castor
The Sickle
CANCER
GEMINI
VIRGO
TAURUS
Pollux
Aldebaran
LEO
Ecliptic
24 Feb
ORION
3 Feb
Regulus
27 Feb
Bellatrix
Betelgeuse
Alnilam
Mintaka
Alnitak
Procyon
Orion Nebula
ERIDANUS
CANIS MINOR
HYDRA
Rigel
Saiph
LEPUS
Sirius
THE MILKY WAY
SE
SW
PUPPIS
CANIS MAJOR
Adhara
LOOKING SOUTH

FEBRUARY

The winter star patterns are drifting westward, as a result of our annual orbit around the Sun. Imagine: you're whirling round on a fairground carousel, and looking out around you. At times you spot the ghost train, sometimes you see the roller-coaster, and then you swing past the candy-floss stall. So it is with the sky: as we circle our local star, we get to see different stars and constellations with the changing seasons.

FEBRUARY'S CONSTELLATION

Spectacular **Orion** is one of the rare star groupings that looks like its namesake – a giant hunter with a sword below his belt, wielding a club above his head.

The seven main stars of this brilliant constellation lie in the 'top 70' brightest stars in the sky. Despite its distinctive shape, most of these stars are not closely associated with each other – they simply line up, one behind the other.

Closest, at 250 light years, is the fainter of the two stars forming the hunter's shoulders, **Bellatrix**. Next in the hierarchy of Orion's superstars is the other shoulder-star, blood-red **Betelgeuse**. This giant star, 640 light years away, is a thousand times larger than our Sun, and its fate will be to explode as a supernova (see November's Topic).

Slightly more brilliant than Betelgeuse, blue-white **Rigel** (Orion's foot), is a vigorous young star more than twice as hot as our Sun, and 125,000 times more luminous. Rigel lies around 860 light years from us.

Saiph, marking the hunter's other foot, is 650 light years distant The two outer stars of the belt, **Alnitak** (left) and **Mintaka** (right) lie 700 and 690 light years away, respectively.

We travel 1300 light years from home to reach the middle star of the belt, **Alnilam**, and the stars of the 'sword' hanging below the belt – the lair of the great **Orion Nebula** (see this month's Object).

FEBRUARY'S OBJECT

Below Orion's Belt lies a fuzzy patch – easily visible to the unaided eye in dark skies. Through binoculars or a small telescope the patch looks like a small cloud in space. It is a cloud, but at 24 light years across, it's hardly petite. Only the distance of the **Orion Nebula** – 1300 light years – diminishes it. It's part of a vast region of starbirth in Orion, and the nearest region to Earth where heavyweight stars are being born. This 'star factory' contains at least 700 fledgling stars, which have just hatched out of immense dark clouds of dust and gas; most are visible only with a telescope that picks up infrared (heat) radiation.

FEBRUARY'S TOPIC: STAR NAMES

Why do the brightest stars have such strange names? Some are lost in the mists of time, dating back millennia to the Babylonians, who drew up many of our constellations. The Greeks took up the baton after that, and the name of the star Antares is a direct result. It means 'rival of Ares' because its red colour rivals that of the planet Mars ('Ares' in Greek).

OBSERVING TIP

It's best to view your favourite objects when they're well clear of the horizon. If you observe them low down, you're looking through a large thickness of the atmosphere, which is always shifting and turbulent. It's like trying to observe the outside world from the bottom of a swimming pool! This turbulence makes the stars appear to twinkle. Low-down planets also twinkle – although to a lesser extent, because they subtend tiny discs, and aren't so affected.

But the Arabs were mainly responsible for the star names we have inherited today. Working in the so-called 'Dark Ages' between the sixth and tenth centuries AD, they took over the naming of the sky – hence the number of stars beginning with the letters 'al' (Arabic for 'the'). **Algol**, in the constellation **Perseus**, means 'the demon' – possibly because the Arabs noticed that its brightness seems to 'wink' every few days. **Deneb**, in **Cygnus**, also has Arabic roots, meaning 'the tail (of the flying bird)'.

The most famous star in the sky has to be **Betelgeuse**, known to generations of schoolkids as 'Beetlejuice'. Until recently, it was gloriously interpreted to mean 'the armpit of the sacred one'. But the 'B' in Betelgeuse turned out to be a mistransliteration of an Arabic letter, and the name probably just means 'Orion's hand'.

FEBRUARY'S PICTURE

'The Old Moon in the New Moon's arms': it's a delightful old phrase, but the reality is more prosaic. The faint glow in this image – earthshine – is light from the sunlit side of Earth, illuminating the Moon's night side. You don't see it every time the Moon is in the sky, because a lot depends on Earth's meteorology. If it's largely clear, the oceans rule our planet's brightness – and water doesn't reflect sunlight well. Clouds, however, can reflect up to 50 per cent, so brighter earthshine tells us that our planet is suffering cloudy conditions. Some scientists monitor the Earth's cloudiness by observing earthshine, which provides a guide to the development of the Greenhouse Effect. And to think that Leonardo da Vinci had worked all this out 500 years ago!

John Bell of Milton Keynes photographed the crescent Moon on 11 February 2016 through his 200 mm Ritchey-Chrétien-type reflector with a Canon 5D MarkII DSLR camera. Using Photoshop, he merged an exposure of 1/20 second for the bright crescent and a 6-second exposure of the rest of the disc, illuminated by faint earthshine. (You'll see a similar phase this year on 18 February.)

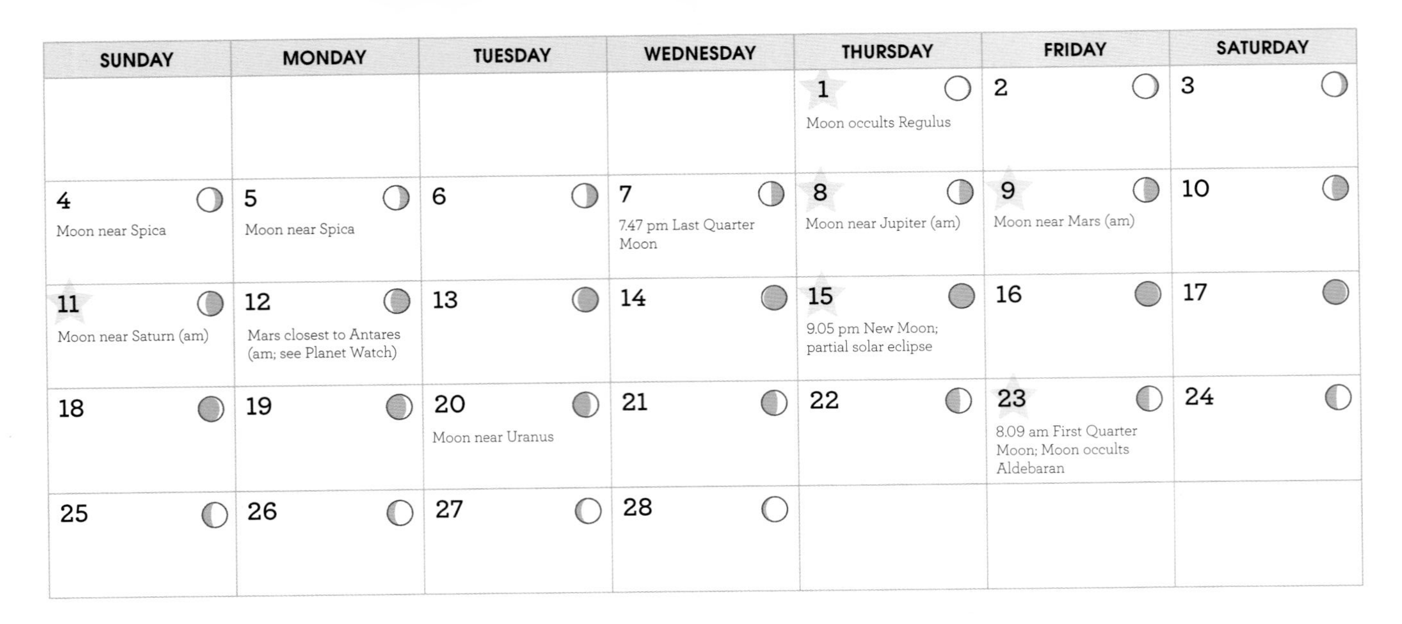

SUNDAY	MONDAY	TUESDAY	WEDNESDAY	THURSDAY	FRIDAY	SATURDAY
				1 Moon occults Regulus	2	3
4 Moon near Spica	5 Moon near Spica	6	7 7.47 pm Last Quarter Moon	8 Moon near Jupiter (am)	9 Moon near Mars (am)	10
11 Moon near Saturn (am)	12 Mars closest to Antares (am; see Planet Watch)	13	14	15 9.05 pm New Moon; partial solar eclipse	16	17
18	19	20 Moon near Uranus	21	22	23 8.09 am First Quarter Moon; Moon occults Aldebaran	24
25	26	27	28			

SPECIAL EVENTS

- **1 February:** from northern Scotland, Regulus is hidden behind the Moon as it rises at about 6 pm; the star reappears around 6.20 pm. Observers in the rest of the British Isles will see the Moon very close to Regulus.
- **8, 9 and 11 February:** in the morning sky, the Moon passes close to Jupiter, Mars and Saturn (Chart 2a).
- **15 February:** Antarctica and the southern regions of South America will witness a partial eclipse of the Sun; it's not visible from the UK.
- **23 February:** Aldebaran is hidden behind the Moon as it grows dark. The exact time it reappears depends on your location, ranging from 5.34 pm in Cork to 5.45 pm in London (Chart 2b) and 5.47 pm in Aberdeen.

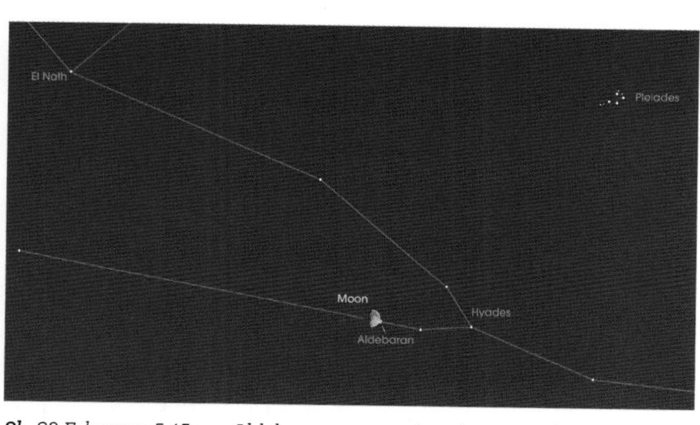

2a 7–11 February, 6 am. The Moon passes Jupiter, Mars and Saturn.

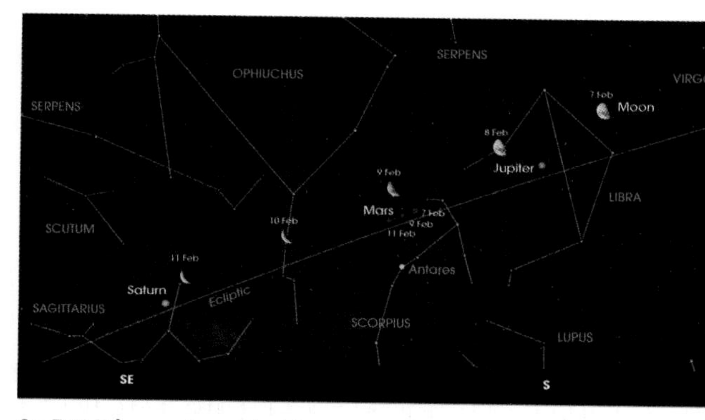

2b 23 February, 5.45 pm. Aldebaran emerges from lunar occultation.

• There's a parade of planets in the early morning sky, led by giant planet **Jupiter**. Rising around 1 am, Jupiter lords it over the constellation Libra, dazzling at magnitude –2.1.

• **Mars** lies to Jupiter's lower left, and rises about 3 am. During February, the Red Planet hurries through the constellation of Scorpius, passing closest to its brightest star – the red giant Antares – on **12 February**. This star is similar in brightness to the Red Planet (both magnitude +1.0), and its name means 'rival of Mars'. Compare their colours (best with binoculars) and decide which should carry off the ruddy laurels!

• After 5 am, you'll find **Saturn** positioned to the lower left of Mars, in Sagittarius. The ringworld shines at magnitude +0.6.

• Meanwhile, the evening sky is pretty dull at the start of the month. **Uranus** (magnitude +5.8) lies in Pisces and sets about 11 pm. Lower down, **Neptune** skulks in Aquarius at magnitude +7.9: setting around 7 pm, it disappears into the twilight glow in mid-February.

• In the second half of the month, the dusk sky is miraculously transformed, as brilliant **Venus** bursts on to the scene on the western horizon. The Evening Star blazes at magnitude –3.9, and by the end of February is setting an hour after the Sun.

• It's joined in the last couple of days of the month by **Mercury**, lying to the lower right of Venus and ten times fainter, at magnitude –1.4.

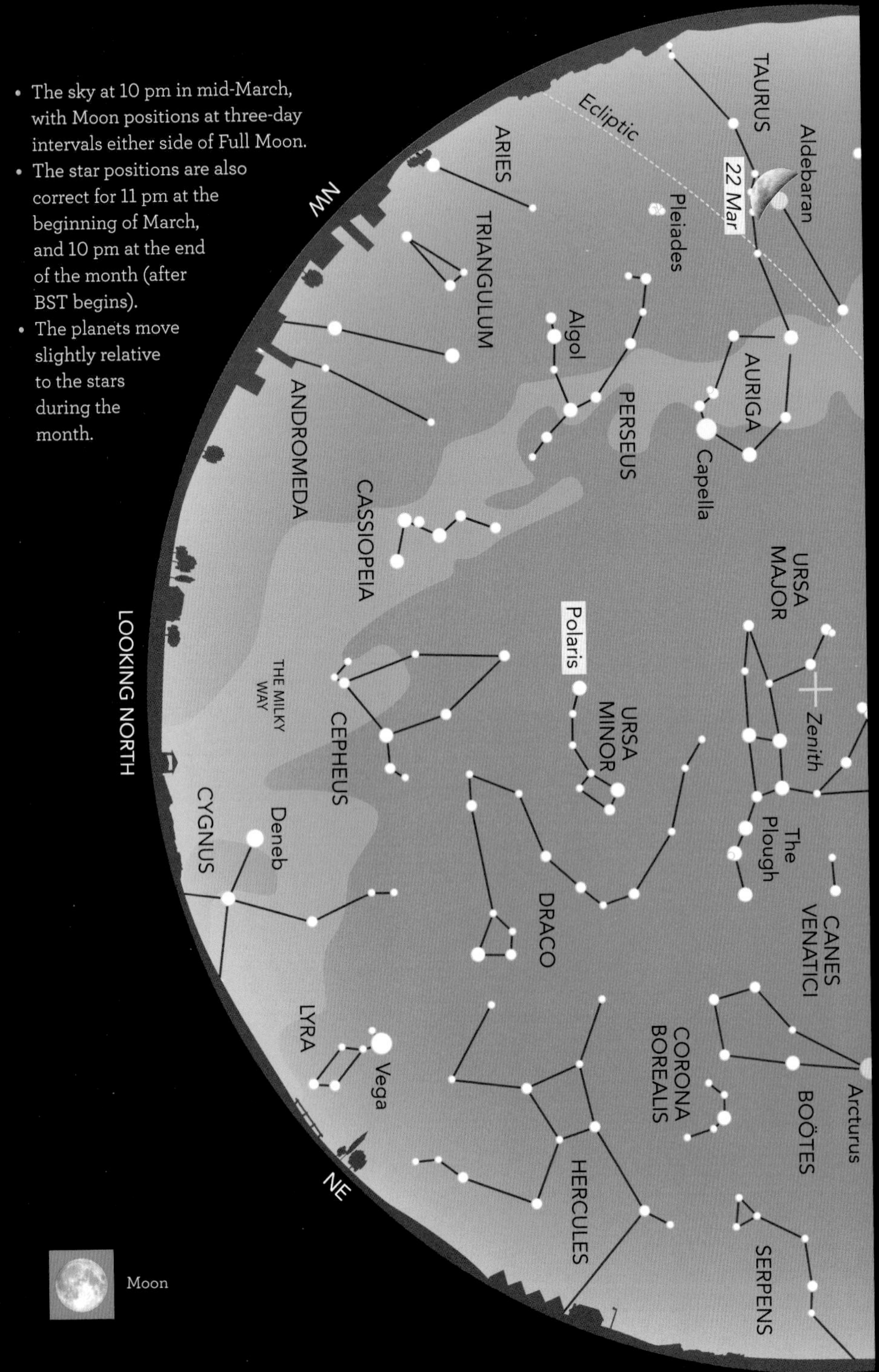

- The sky at 10 pm in mid-March, with Moon positions at three-day intervals either side of Full Moon.
- The star positions are also correct for 11 pm at the beginning of March, and 10 pm at the end of the month (after BST begins).
- The planets move slightly relative to the stars during the month.

EAST
WEST
SERPENS
BOÖTES
Arcturus
CANES VENATICI
Zenith
URSA MAJOR
AURIGA
22 Mar
Aldebaran
TAURUS
GEMINI
Castor
Pollux
The Sickle
Denebola
Algieba
LEO
VIRGO
Regulus
28 Mar
CANCER
25 Mar
Betelgeuse
ERIDANUS
ORION
Rigel
Procyon
CANIS MINOR
Ecliptic
Spica
31 Mar
2 Mar
LEPUS
THE MILKY WAY
Sirius
CORVUS
HYDRA
CANIS MAJOR
PUPPIS
SE
SW
LOOKING SOUTH
MARCH

There's a plethora of reasons to celebrate in March. It's the best month this year to spot the elusive planet **Mercury**, using its bigger sister Venus as a landmark. Plus, the spring has sprung: on 20 March, we celebrate the Equinox, when day becomes longer than the night, and British Summer Time starts on 25 March.

MARCH'S CONSTELLATION

Like the fabled hunter Orion, **Leo** is one of the rare constellations that resembles the real thing – in this case, a huge crouching lion. Among the oldest constellations, Leo commemorates the giant Nemean lion slaughtered by Hercules as the first of his 12 labours. According to legend, the lion's flesh couldn't be pierced by iron, stone or bronze – so Hercules wrestled with the beast and choked it to death.

The lion's heart is marked by the first magnitude star **Regulus**. This celestial whirling dervish spins around in just 16 hours, making its equator bulge remarkably. Rising upwards is **'the Sickle'**, a back-to-front question mark that delineates the front quarters, neck and head of Leo. A small telescope shows that **Algieba**, the star that makes up the lion's shoulder, is actually a beautiful close double star.

OBSERVING TIP

This is the ideal time of year to tie down the main compass directions, as seen from your observing site. North is easy – just latch onto Polaris, the Pole Star (see December's Object). And at noon, the Sun is always in the south. But the useful extra in March is that we hit the Spring Equinox, when the Sun rises due east, and sets due west. So remember those positions relative to a tree or house around your horizon.

The other end of Leo is home to **Denebola**, which means in Arabic 'the lion's tail'. Just underneath the main 'body' of Leo are several spiral galaxies – nearby cities of stars like our own Milky Way. They can't be seen with the unaided eye, but sweep along the lion's tummy with a small telescope to reveal them.

MARCH'S OBJECT

This is your best chance to see tiny **Mercury** this year. In mid-March, the little runt of the Solar System sets 1 hour 50 minutes after the Sun.

This tiny world – just a little bigger than our Moon – is covered in craters. But that's where the resemblance ends. NASA's Messenger spaceprobe discovered that Mercury has a huge core made of molten iron. As the core cooled, the planet shrank, wrinkling its surface like the skin of a dried-up apple. But why should a small world have such a large core? It could be that, during its origins, a collision with another planet blasted off most of its outer rocky layers.

And Messenger's mission highlighted other anomalies. Mercury has a magnetic field; unheard of on a world so small. And, most controversially, Messenger detected traces of water vapour at Mercury's poles. Although the planet has temperatures that range up to 700°C, the cold mountains at Mercury's poles never see sunlight.

About to tackle all these mysteries is the European spaceprobe BepiColombo. It's due to be launched in October – and it will no doubt bring us more surprises about this oddball little world.

The aurora borealis photographed from Blyth Harbour, Northumberland, on 27 February 2015. Anita Nicholson used a Canon 5D MarkII DSLR camera with 50 mm f/1.8 lens to give a 5-second exposure at ISO 5000.

MARCH'S TOPIC: PULSARS

It was a signal so weird that the discoverers labelled it 'LGM-1'; perhaps the first communication from 'Little Green Men'. The radio astronomers at Cambridge, in 1967, had detected a regular stream of radio pulses, once every 1.337 seconds. It wasn't coming from an alien intelligence, however, but something almost as outlandish: a pulsar.

We now know a pulsar is the collapsed core of an old star that has exploded as a supernova. It's composed entirely of tiny subatomic particles called neutrons, so tightly packed that a pulsar (also called a neutron star) contains as much matter as the Sun, in a ball no bigger than London!

A pinhead of its material would weigh as much as a fully laden supertanker, and its gravity is so strong you'd expend more effort climbing a one-centimetre hump than in ascending Mount Everest on Earth. A typical pulsar has a fearsome magnetic field, a thousand billion times stronger than Earth's magnetism. As it spins round, beams of radiation sweep around like a lighthouse beacon, creating the radio pulses we detect.

'LGM-1' spins round in just over a second. The most extreme pulsar, J1748-2446ad, is rotating an amazing 716 times per second – faster than a kitchen blender!

MARCH'S PICTURE

Aurorae (the Northern and Southern Lights) take place when the Sun has a magnetic storm. Charged particles rush towards Earth's magnetic poles, and light up the sky like gas in a neon tube. The heavens glow with sensational, shifting curtains and rays. Its glorious colours come from the elements in the atmosphere, energised by the Sun's particles: high-altitude oxygen glows red, medium-level oxygen gives the aurora its characteristic green colour, while nitrogen provides the blue and red-purple tinges.

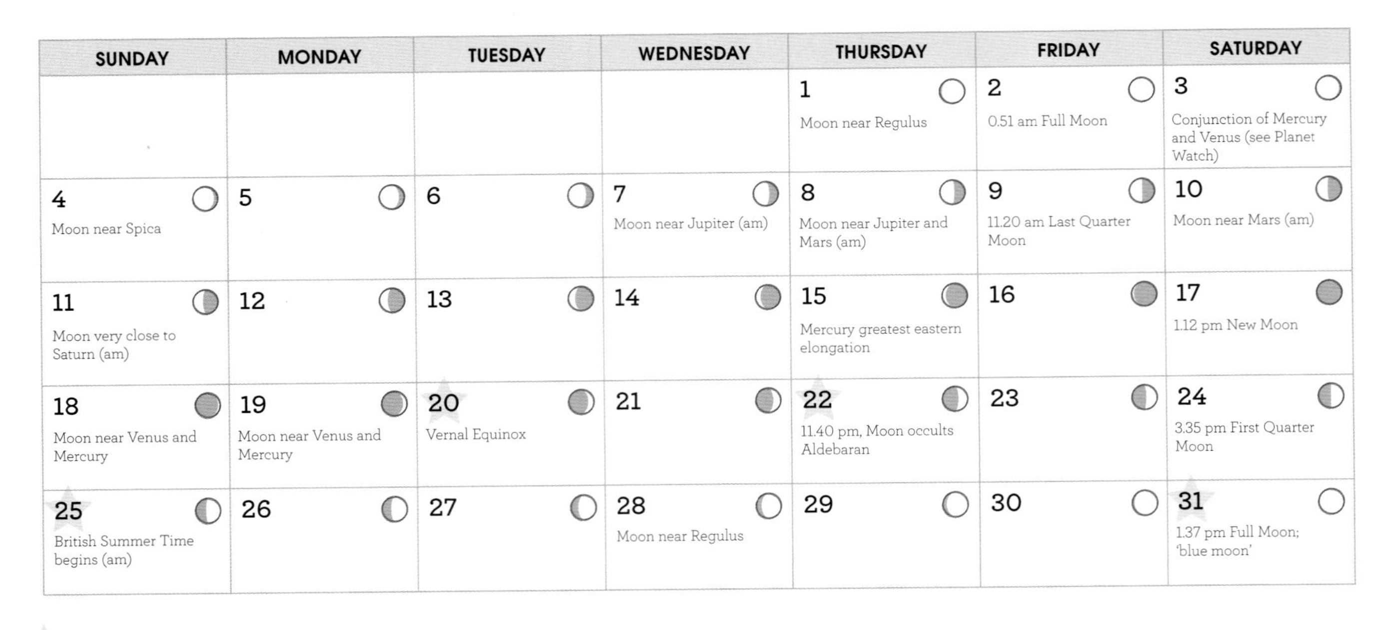

SUNDAY	MONDAY	TUESDAY	WEDNESDAY	THURSDAY	FRIDAY	SATURDAY
				1 Moon near Regulus	2 0.51 am Full Moon	3 Conjunction of Mercury and Venus (see Planet Watch)
4 Moon near Spica	5	6	7 Moon near Jupiter (am)	8 Moon near Jupiter and Mars (am)	9 11.20 am Last Quarter Moon	10 Moon near Mars (am)
11 Moon very close to Saturn (am)	12	13	14	15 Mercury greatest eastern elongation	16	17 1.12 pm New Moon
18 Moon near Venus and Mercury	19 Moon near Venus and Mercury	20 Vernal Equinox	21	22 11.40 pm, Moon occults Aldebaran	23	24 3.35 pm First Quarter Moon
25 British Summer Time begins (am)	26	27	28 Moon near Regulus	29	30	31 1.37 pm Full Moon; 'blue moon'

SPECIAL EVENTS

- **20 March, 4.15 pm:** the Vernal Equinox marks the beginning of spring, as the Sun moves up to shine over the northern hemisphere.
- **22 March:** as the sky grows dark, at around 7.30 pm, the Moon is right in front of the Hyades star cluster (best seen through binoculars). During the evening, it moves in front of some of the fainter stars; then – at 11.40 pm (exact time depends on your location) – the Moon occults bright Aldebaran (Chart 3b).
- **25 March, 1.00 am:** British Summer Time starts – don't forget to put your clocks forward (the mnemonic is 'Spring forward, Fall back').
- **31 March:** the second 'blue moon' of the year, when two Full Moons occur in the same month (see January's Topic).
- This month, NASA plans to launch the Transiting Exoplanet Survey Satellite, to search for Earth-like planets in orbit around nearby stars.

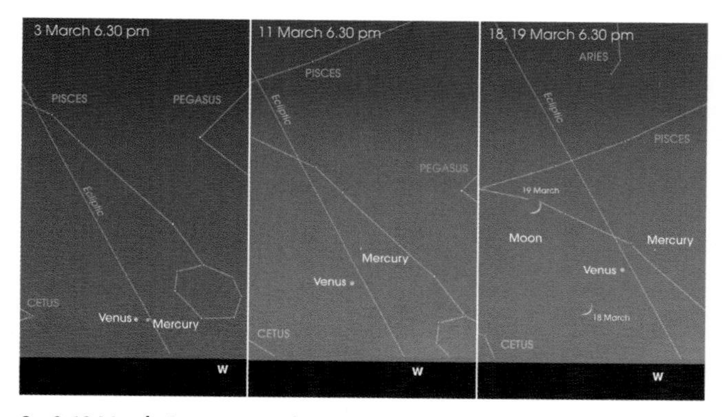

3a *3–19 March. Conjunction of Mercury and Venus; crescent Moon.*

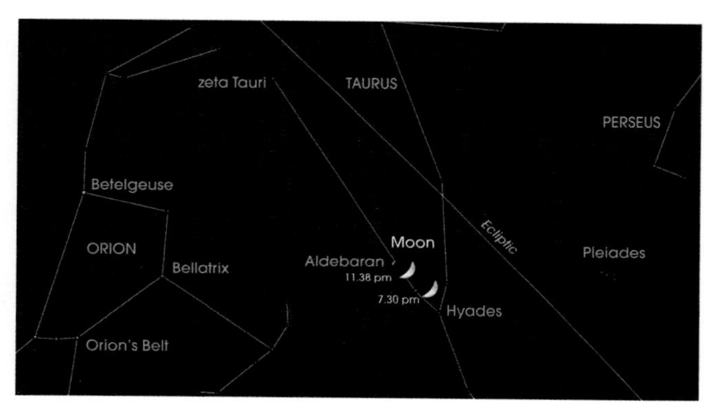

3b *22 March, 7.30–11.38 pm. The Moon occults the Hyades and Aldebaran.*

- Look low in the west after sunset, for a planetary waltz that lasts most of the month. Leading the dance is **Venus**, at magnitude –3.9, which is setting two hours after the Sun as the brilliant Evening Star. Fainter **Mercury** swings round its partner, starting March to the lower right of Venus, rising upwards until mid-month and then sinking back down. This little world fades throughout March, starting at –1.3 (ten times fainter than Venus) and fading into the twilight glow at magnitude +1 by **20 March**. On **3 March** you'll find Mercury just a degree to the right of Venus – an ideal time to spot the elusive planet – while the crescent Moon joins the dance partners on **18 and 19 March** (Chart 3a).
- On **28 March**, use Venus as a signpost to another faint planet: that evening, **Uranus** lies just half a degree above the Evening Star. It's on the verge of naked eye visibility, at magnitude +5.9, but will be easy to snare through binoculars or a small telescope. Uranus lies in Pisces all month, setting around 9 pm.
- Around 11.30 pm, **Jupiter** rises in Libra, at a glorious magnitude –2.2. It's followed by fainter **Mars** (magnitude +0.6), rising at about 2.30 am: during March, the Red Planet treks from Ophiuchus to Sagittarius. By the end of the month, Mars is closing on in **Saturn**, similar in brightness at magnitude +0.5 in Sagittarius, and rising around 3 am.
- **Neptune** is lost in the Sun's glare this month.

- The sky at 11 pm in mid-April, with Moon positions at three-day intervals either side of Full Moon.
- The star positions are also correct for midnight at the beginning of April, and 10 pm at the end of the month.
- The planets move slightly relative to the stars during the month.

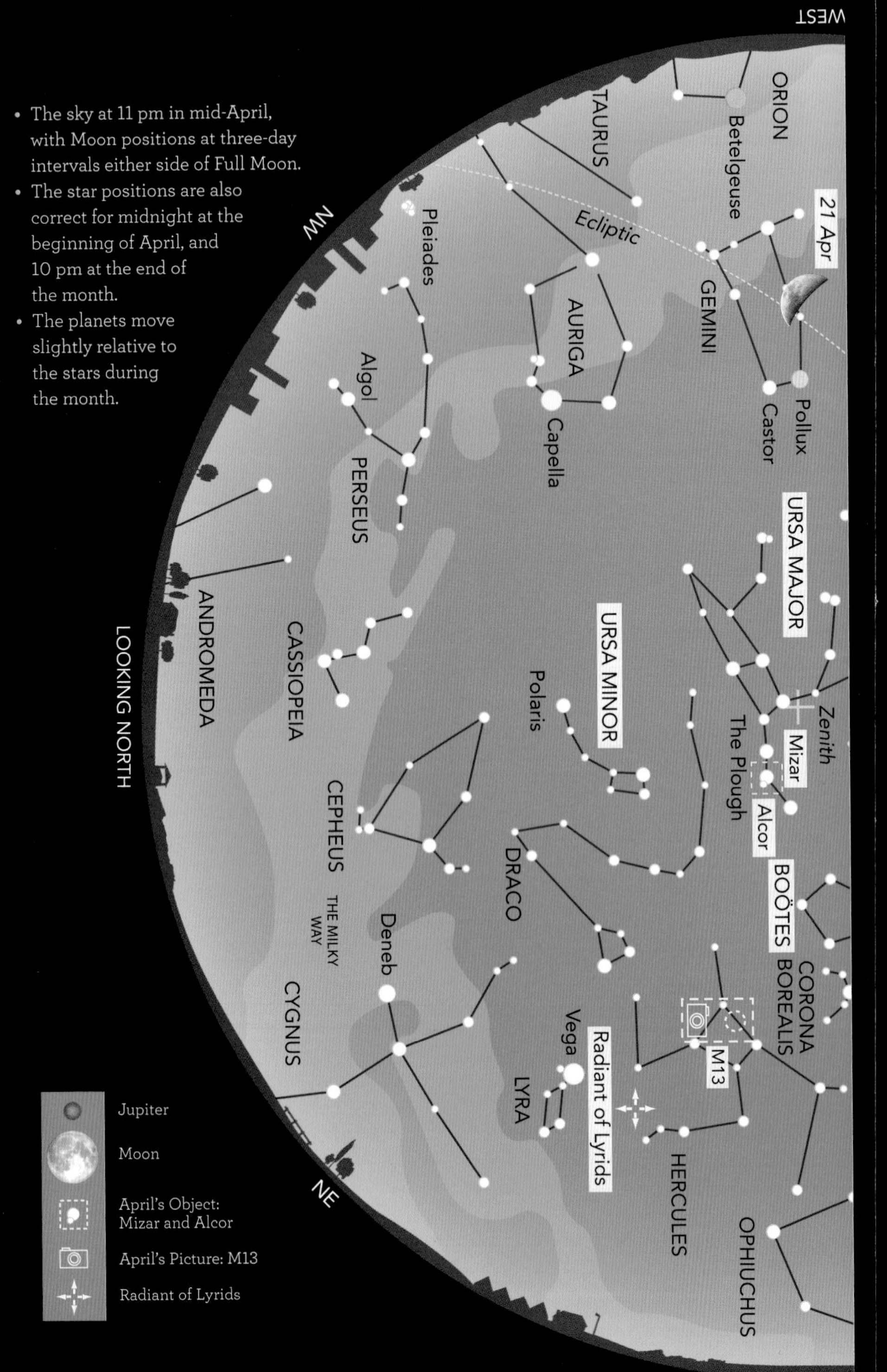

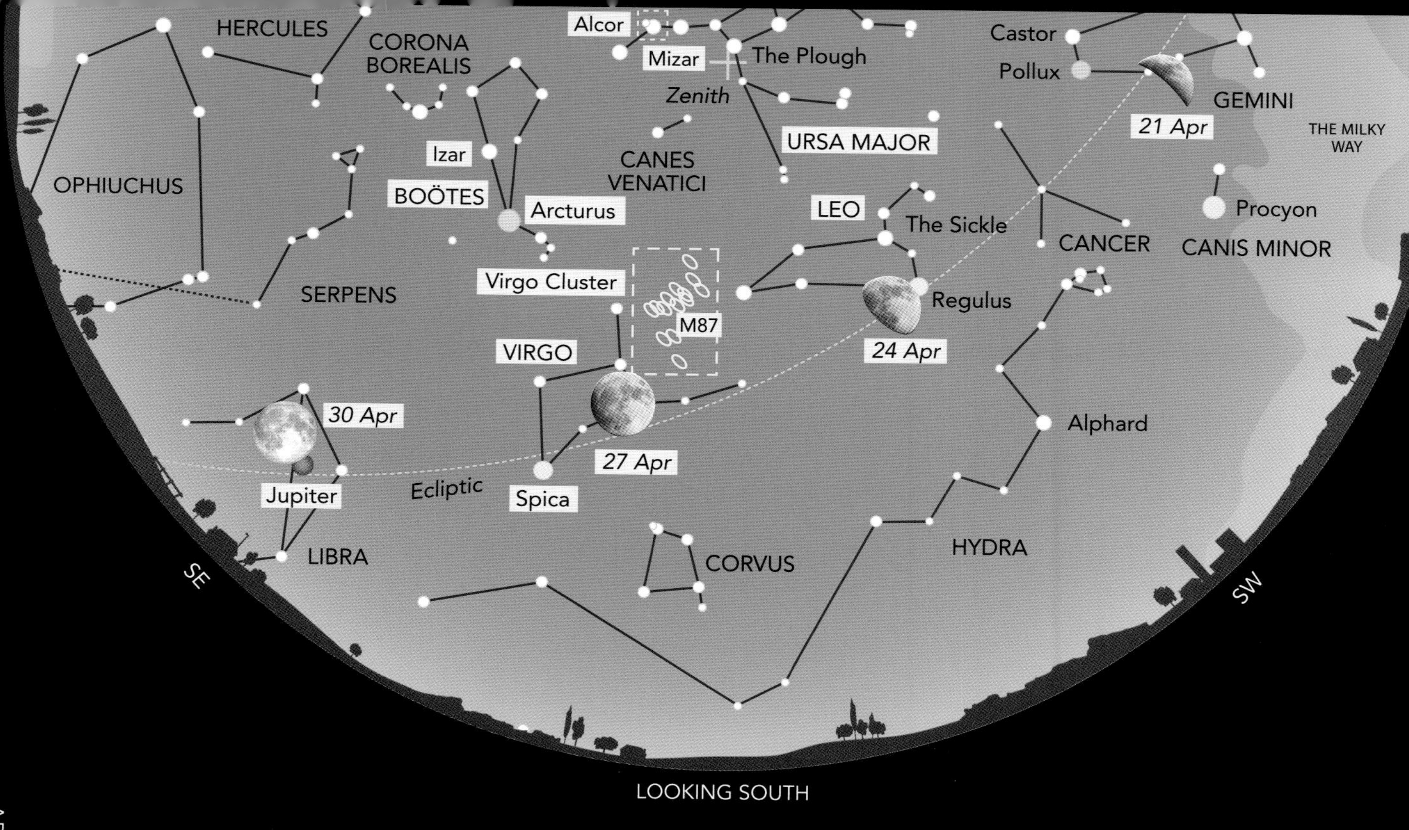

EAST
WEST
HERCULES
CORONA BOREALIS
Alcor
Mizar
The Plough
Zenith
Castor
Pollux
GEMINI
21 Apr
THE MILKY WAY
OPHIUCHUS
Izar
BOÖTES
Arcturus
CANES VENATICI
URSA MAJOR
LEO
The Sickle
CANCER
Procyon
CANIS MINOR
SERPENS
Virgo Cluster
M87
Regulus
24 Apr
VIRGO
30 Apr
27 Apr
Alphard
Jupiter
Ecliptic
Spica
LIBRA
CORVUS
HYDRA
SE
SW
LOOKING SOUTH

APRIL

The ancient constellations of **Leo** and **Virgo** dominate the springtime skies. Leo does indeed look like a recumbent lion, but it's hard to envisage Virgo as anything other than a vast 'Y' in the sky!

APRIL'S CONSTELLATION

Boötes (the Herdsman) is shaped rather like a kite. It was mentioned in Homer's *Odyssey*, and its name refers to the fact that Boötes seems to 'herd' the stars that lie in the northern part of the sky.

The name of the brightest star, **Arcturus**, means 'bear-driver'. It apparently 'drives' the two bears (**Ursa Major** and **Ursa Minor**) around the sky as the Earth rotates. Arcturus is the fourth brightest star in the whole sky, and it's the most brilliant star you can see on May evenings. A red giant star in its old age, Arcturus lies 37 light years from us, and shines 170 times more brilliantly than the Sun.

The star at the ten o'clock position from Arcturus is called **Izar**, meaning 'the belt'. Through a good telescope, it appears as a gorgeous double star – one star yellow and the other blue.

APRIL'S OBJECT

Home in on the 'kink' in the tail of Ursa Major (the Great Bear), and you'll spot the most famous pair of stars in the sky – **Mizar** (magnitude +2.4) and **Alcor** (magnitude +4.0). Generations of astronomers have referred to them as 'the horse and rider', and most popular books say they are orbiting each other.

But *are* Mizar and Alcor an item – perhaps Alcor just happens to lie in front of Mizar? This subject has been a bone of contention among astronomers for decades. The most recent measurements, however, put them at very much the same distance from us: 82 light years for Alcor and 83 for Mizar, so they are almost certainly in a gravitational embrace. But it's not a simple double star system. Mizar has a companion that's visible through a telescope, and both these stars are actually double, making four stars in all. And Alcor has a very faint companion, too – so there's a total of six stars making up this amazing system.

APRIL'S TOPIC: CLUSTERS OF GALAXIES

Sweep the 'bowl' of Virgo's Y-shape with a small telescope, and you'll unearth quite a few 'faint fuzzies'. These are just a handful of the thousands of galaxies making up the **Virgo Cluster**: our closest giant cluster of galaxies, lying at a distance of 54 million light years.

Galaxies are gregarious. Thanks to gravity, they like living in groups. The Milky Way and our neighbouring giant spiral, the Andromeda Galaxy,

OBSERVING TIP

Venus is a real treat this month. Through a small telescope, you'll be able to make out its gibbous shape. But don't wait for the sky to get totally dark. Seen against a black sky, the cloud-wreathed world is so brilliant it's difficult to make out any details. You're best off viewing Venus soon after the Sun has set, when the Evening Star first becomes visible in the twilight glow. Through a telescope, the planet then appears less dazzling against a pale blue sky.

From his home in Essex, Nik Symanek photographed the globular cluster M13 by remote observing using the 2-metre Faulkes Telescope North in Hawaii. He needed four separate panes to show the whole cluster, with five 90-second sub-exposures for each of the red, green and blue filters.

are members of a small cluster of about 30 smallish galaxies called the Local Group. But the Virgo Cluster is in a different league: it's like a vast galactic swarm of bees. What's more, its enormous gravity holds sway over the smaller groups around – including our Local Group – making up a cluster of clusters of galaxies, the Virgo Supercluster.

Many of the galaxies in the Virgo Cluster are spirals like our Milky Way, but some are even more spectacular. The heavyweight is **M87**, a giant of a galaxy that's blasting out a jet of gas over 5000 light years long.

Though the Virgo Cluster seems massive, weighing as much as a million billion Suns, some distant clusters are more monstrous – up to ten times heavier still. The biggest clusters often look more boring, though, as they largely comprise bland elliptical galaxies rather than stately spirals.

Galaxy clusters and superclusters are the salt of the Universe. They make up the structure of the Cosmos, with huge filaments of superclusters enclosing enormous empty voids – like a gigantic Swiss cheese.

APRIL'S PICTURE

The Great Globular Cluster in Hercules (**M13**) is a compact ball of over 300,000 stars, containing some of the oldest citizens of the Galaxy. With an age of 12 billion years, its stars were born soon after the Big Bang – so astronomers are keen to study them to get a picture of the early Universe. M13 is just one of over 150 globular clusters surrounding our Milky Way. The cluster itself – discovered by Edmond Halley in 1714 – is 145 light years across, and lies 26,000 light years away. It is just visible to the unaided eye.

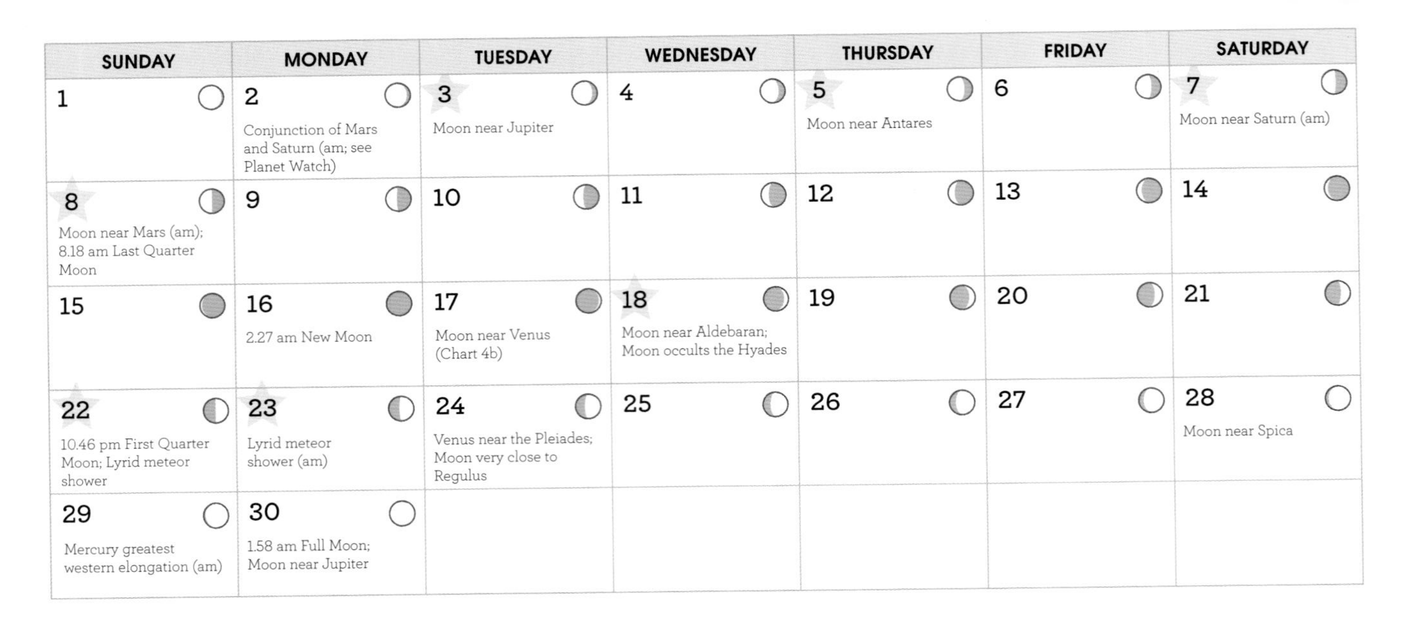

SUNDAY	MONDAY	TUESDAY	WEDNESDAY	THURSDAY	FRIDAY	SATURDAY
1	2 Conjunction of Mars and Saturn (am; see Planet Watch)	3 Moon near Jupiter	4	5 Moon near Antares	6	7 Moon near Saturn (am)
8 Moon near Mars (am); 8.18 am Last Quarter Moon	9	10	11	12	13	14
15	16 2.27 am New Moon	17 Moon near Venus (Chart 4b)	18 Moon near Aldebaran; Moon occults the Hyades	19	20	21
22 10.46 pm First Quarter Moon; Lyrid meteor shower	23 Lyrid meteor shower (am)	24 Venus near the Pleiades; Moon very close to Regulus	25	26	27	28 Moon near Spica
29 Mercury greatest western elongation (am)	30 1.58 am Full Moon; Moon near Jupiter					

SPECIAL EVENTS

- **3, 5, 7, 8 April:** the Moon passes Jupiter, Antares, Saturn and Mars (Chart 4a).
- **18 April:** the Moon starts to occult the Hyades star cluster around 11 pm (exact time depends on your location) just before it sets (Chart 4b).
- **Night of 22/23 April:** maximum of the **Lyrid** meteor shower, which appears to emanate from the constellation of Lyra. The meteors are dusty debris from Comet Thatcher, burning up in the Earth's atmosphere. Best to observe in the early hours of the morning, after the Moon has set.

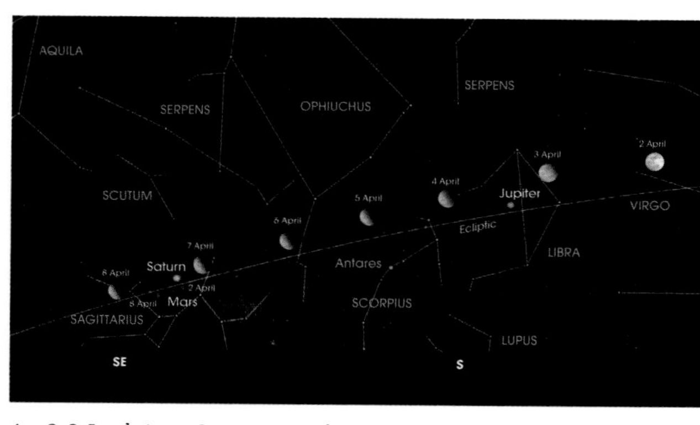

4a *2–8 April, 4 am. Conjunction of Mars and Saturn; the Moon passes Jupiter, Saturn and Mars.*

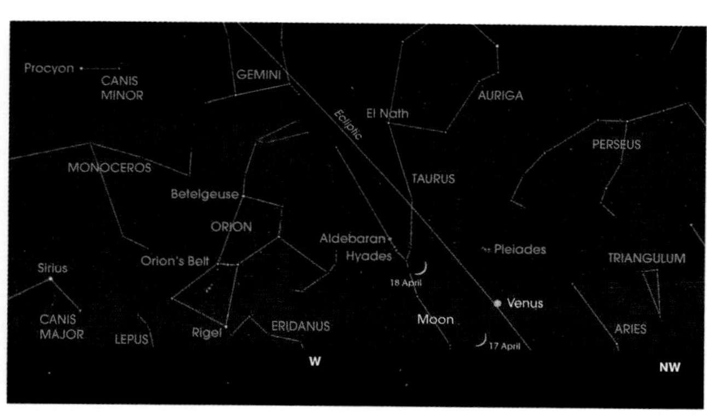

4b *17–18 April, 9.30 pm. Crescent Moon with Venus, the Pleiades and the Hyades.*

Venus

- You can't miss **Venus**, shining splendiferously in the western sky after sunset, at magnitude –3.9 (Chart 4b). By the end of April, the Evening Star is setting two-and-a-half hours after the Sun, and you'll see it against a totally dark sky just before it sinks below the horizon.
- Mighty **Jupiter** is rising in the south-east around 10 pm, its magnitude –2.4 brilliance livening up the dim constellation Libra.
- **Mars** and slightly fainter **Saturn** (magnitudes +0.3 and +0.5 respectively) start the month close together in Sagittarius, rising at about 3 am. The two planets pass just over a degree apart during the morning of **2 April** (Chart 4a). Mars then speeds away towards the left, brightening all the time to end the month at magnitude –0.3.
- Dim **Neptune** (magnitude +7.9) lies in Aquarius, and rises in the east around 5 am.
- **Mercury** and **Uranus** are lost in the Sun's glare during April, even though Mercury is at its greatest elongation west of the Sun on **29 April**.

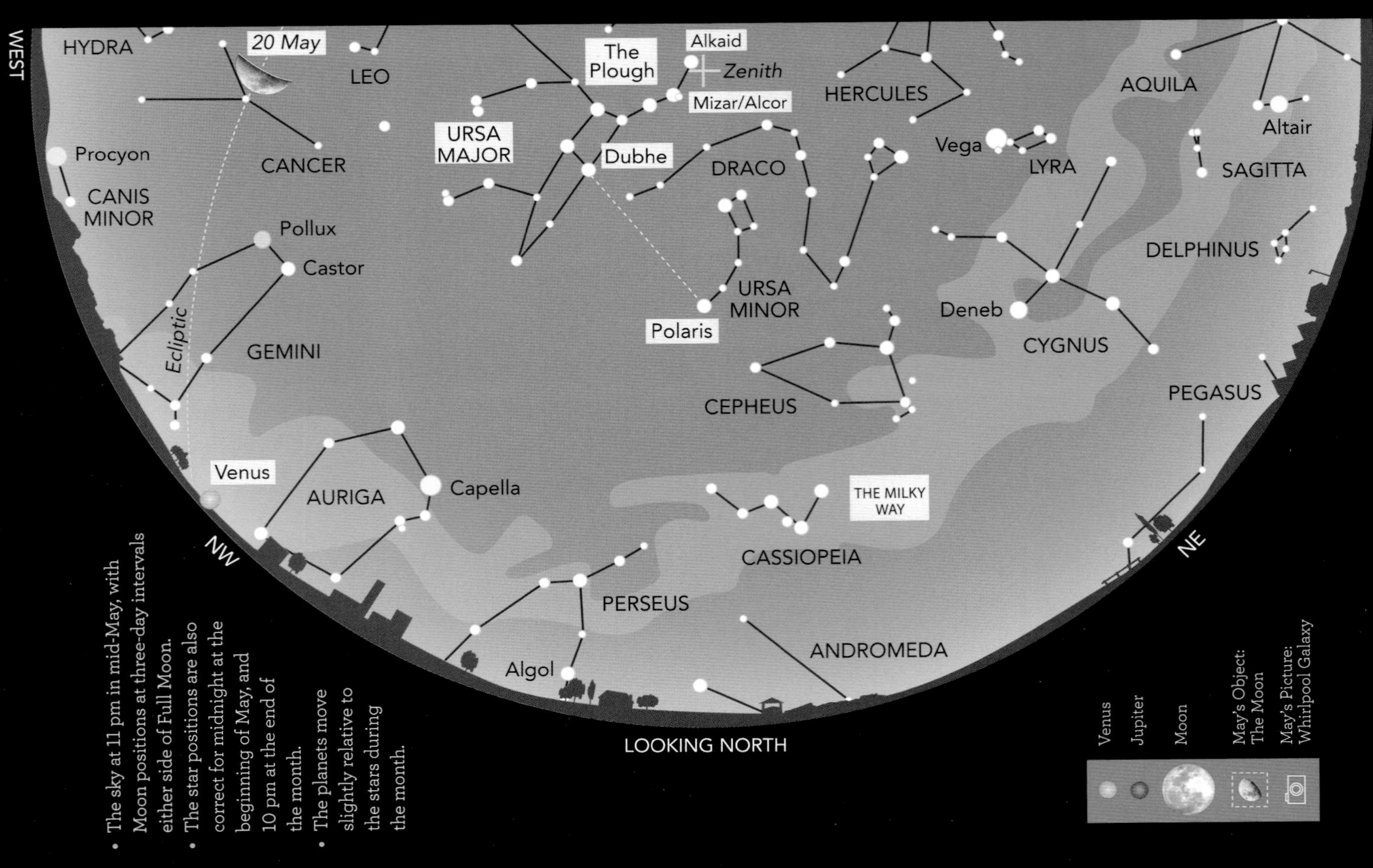

The sky at 11 pm in mid-May, with Moon positions at three-day intervals either side of Full Moon.
The star positions are also correct for midnight at the beginning of May, and 10 pm at the end of the month.
The planets move slightly relative to the stars during the month.
WEST
EAST
NW
NE
LOOKING NORTH
HYDRA
Procyon
CANIS MINOR
Ecliptic
20 May
CANCER
LEO
GEMINI
Pollux
Castor
Venus
AURIGA
Capella
URSA MAJOR
The Plough
Dubhe
Alkaid
Mizar/Alcor
Zenith
Polaris
URSA MINOR
DRACO
CEPHEUS
Algol
PERSEUS
CASSIOPEIA
THE MILKY WAY
ANDROMEDA
HERCULES
Vega
LYRA
Deneb
CYGNUS
AQUILA
DELPHINUS
SAGITTA
Altair
PEGASUS
Venus
Jupiter
Moon
May's Object: The Moon
May's Picture: Whirlpool Galaxy
MAY

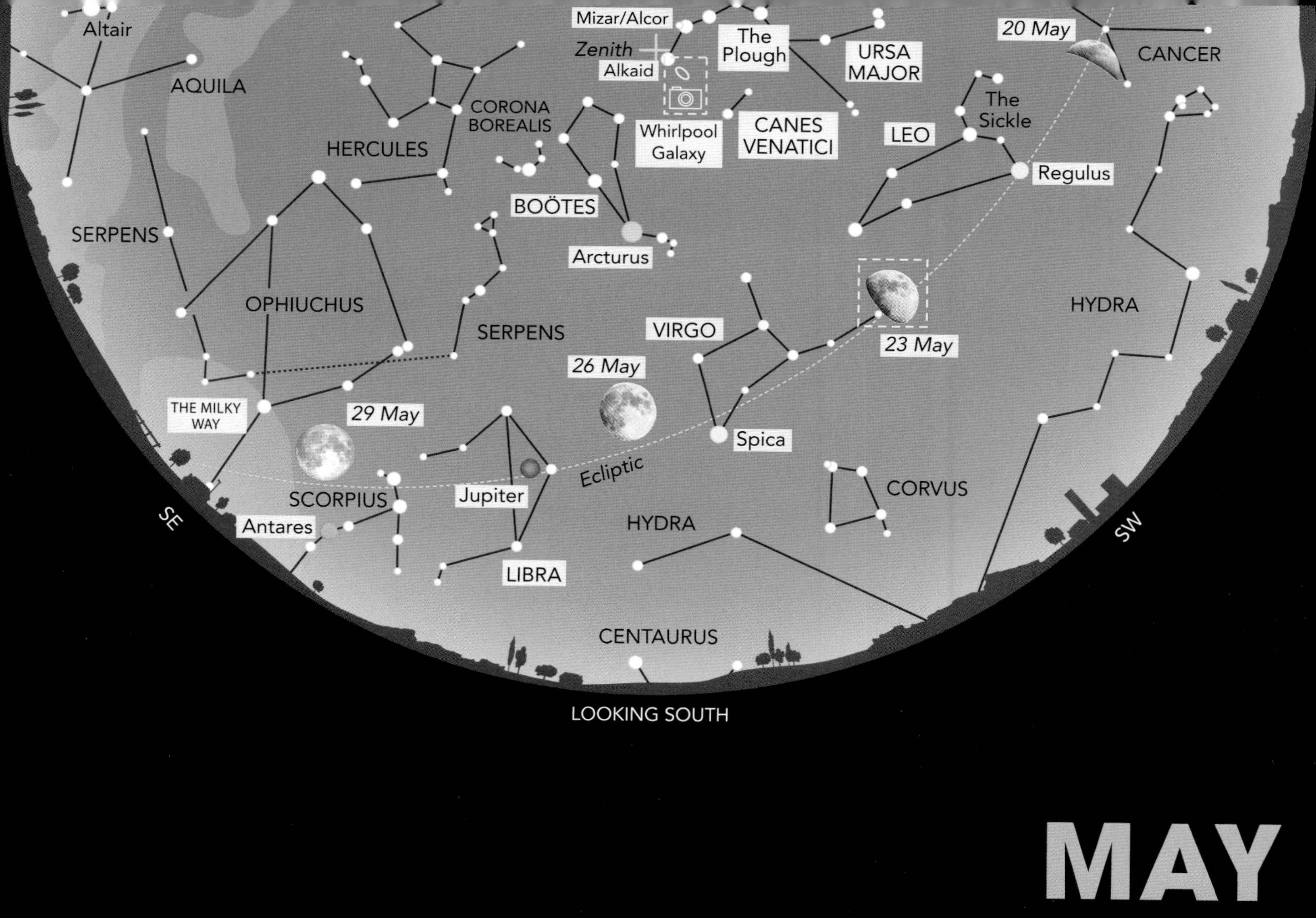
EAST
WEST
Altair
AQUILA
Mizar/Alcor
Zenith
Alkaid
The Plough
URSA MAJOR
20 May
CANCER
The Sickle
CORONA BOREALIS
HERCULES
Whirlpool Galaxy
CANES VENATICI
LEO
Regulus
BOÖTES
SERPENS
Arcturus
OPHIUCHUS
SERPENS
VIRGO
HYDRA
23 May
26 May
THE MILKY WAY
29 May
Spica
Ecliptic
SCORPIUS
Jupiter
CORVUS
SE
Antares
HYDRA
SW
LIBRA
CENTAURUS
LOOKING SOUTH
MAY

Two brilliant planets are vying for attention this month. Gas-giant **Jupiter** is at opposition in May, at its closest and brightest this year. But it can't quite match the brilliance of showy Venus, across the sky in the dusk twilight. Star-wise, orange-coloured **Arcturus**, the principal star of **Boötes** (the Herdsman), forms a giant triangle with two blue-white stars: **Spica**, in **Virgo**, and **Leo**'s shining light **Regulus**.

MAY'S CONSTELLATION

Ursa Major (the Great Bear) is an internationally favourite constellation. In Britain, its seven brightest stars are called **'the Plough'**. Children today generally haven't seen an old-fashioned horse-drawn plough, and we've found them naming this star pattern 'the saucepan'. In North America, it's known as 'the Big Dipper'.

The Plough is the first star pattern that most people get to know. It's always on view in the northern hemisphere, and the two end stars of the 'bowl' of the Plough point directly towards the Pole Star, **Polaris**, which always lies due north (see December's Object).

Ursa Major is unusual in a couple of ways. First, it contains a double star that you can split with the naked eye: **Mizar**, the star in the middle of the bear's tail (or the handle of the saucepan) has a fainter companion, **Alcor** (see April's Object).

And – unlike most constellations – the majority of the stars in the Plough lie at the same distance and were born together. Leaving aside **Dubhe** and **Alkaid**, the others are all moving in the same direction (along with brilliant Sirius, which is also a member of the group). Over thousands of years, the shape of the Plough will gradually change, as Dubhe and Alkaid go off on their own paths.

OBSERVING TIP

It's always fun to search out the 'faint fuzzies' in the sky – galaxies, star clusters and nebulae. But don't even think of observing dark sky objects around the time of Full Moon – its light will drown them out. You'll have the best views near New Moon: a period astronomers call 'dark of Moon'. When the Moon is bright, though, there's still plenty to see: focus on planets, bright double stars and, of course, the Moon itself. Check the Moon phases on the Calendar for each month.

MAY'S OBJECT

The **Moon** is our nearest celestial companion, lying a mere 384,400 kilometres away. At 3476 kilometres across, it's so large compared to Earth that – from space – the system looks like a double planet.

But the Moon couldn't be more different from our verdant Earth. Bereft of an atmosphere, it's constantly exposed to bombardment by meteorites and asteroids. Even with the unaided eye, you can see the evidence. The 'face' of the 'Man in the Moon' consists of huge craters created by asteroid hits 3.8 billion years ago.

Through binoculars or a telescope, the surface of the Moon looks amazing – as if you're flying over it. But don't observe our satellite when it's Full: the light is flat, and swamps its features. It's best to roam the Moon when it's a crescent or half-lit, and see the sideways-on shadows highlighting its dramatic relief.

MAY'S TOPIC: A STAR'S LIFE

We think of the stars as being constant and unchanging, but a leisurely look at the **Milky Way** suggests otherwise... Sweep the glowing band with binoculars, and you'll find it studded with nebulae – gas clouds that are the nurseries of new stars. These fledgling stars grow up to make energetic young stars like **Regulus**, shining as a result of nuclear reactions in their searingly hot cores. As stars age – and their hydrogen fuel starts to run out – they develop the problems of middle age. Look no further than orange **Arcturus** and baleful red **Antares** for stars that have swollen up and cooled down near the end of their lives. Stars like these will eventually puff off their distended atmospheres into space, leaving a brief-lived 'planetary nebula' (like the Helix Nebula in Aquarius; see October's Picture). The nebula will soon disperse, leaving the defunct star's core – a white dwarf – alone in space.

MAY'S PICTURE

The stunning **Whirlpool Galaxy** (M51) – and its companion, NGC 5195 – grace the tiny constellation of **Canes Venatici**. Lying 26 million light years away, the pair are adored by all astronomers. Amateurs love its glorious appearance; professionals greedily analyse its intricate structure. The Whirlpool – only half the size of the Milky Way – harbours a massive black hole at its core.

Some 500 million years ago, NGC 5195 passed through its larger companion, pulling out streamers of gas, and triggering massive starbirth. The heaviest young stars are exploding as supernovae – three in 2016 alone!

Sara Wager of Olocau in Spain used a Celestron 230 mm Schmidt-Cassegrain reflector with an Atik 460EXM camera to capture this image of the Whirlpool Galaxy. Fifty 10-minute mono exposures revealed the faint outer envelope, while a further 50 3-minute exposures through each of red, green and blue filters gave the detail and colour, making a total 15½ hours' exposure.

MAY'S CALENDAR

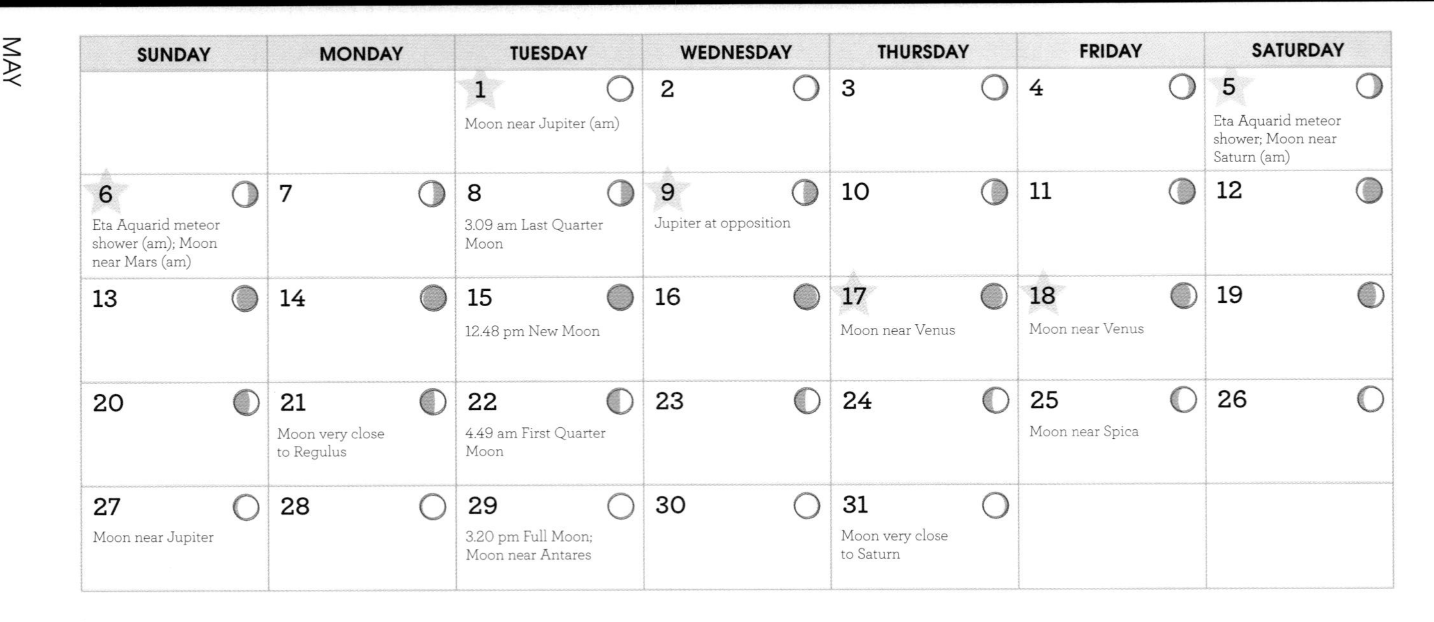

SUNDAY	MONDAY	TUESDAY	WEDNESDAY	THURSDAY	FRIDAY	SATURDAY
		1 Moon near Jupiter (am)	2	3	4	5 Eta Aquarid meteor shower; Moon near Saturn (am)
6 Eta Aquarid meteor shower (am); Moon near Mars (am)	7	8 3.09 am Last Quarter Moon	9 Jupiter at opposition	10	11	12
13	14	15 12.48 pm New Moon	16	17 Moon near Venus	18 Moon near Venus	19
20	21 Moon very close to Regulus	22 4.49 am First Quarter Moon	23	24	25 Moon near Spica	26
27 Moon near Jupiter	28	29 3.20 pm Full Moon; Moon near Antares	30	31 Moon very close to Saturn		

SPECIAL EVENTS

- **1, 5, 6 May:** The Moon passes Jupiter, Saturn and Mars in the morning sky (Chart 5a).
- **Night of 5/6 May:** Shooting stars from the **Eta Aquarid** meteor shower – tiny pieces shed by Halley's Comet burning up in Earth's atmosphere – fly across the sky tonight. You'll have the best views before the Moon rises at 1.30 am.
- **9 May:** Jupiter is opposite to the Sun in the sky. Because the planets' orbits are not quite circular, we are closest to the giant planet the following day, at 658 million km.
- **17–18 May:** There's a glorious sight low in the western sky, with the crescent Moon up close and personal to Venus (Chart 5b).
- This month sees the planned launch of NASA's Insight mission to Mars. The unmanned lander will probe the Red Planet's interior by monitoring Mars-quakes and measuring heat flowing out from deep underground.

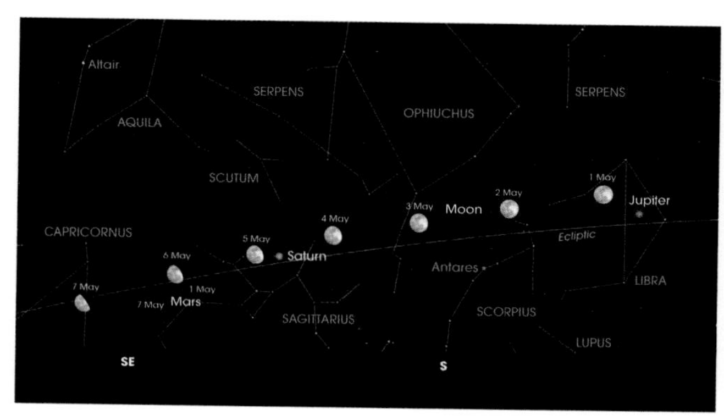

5a 1-7 May, 3 am. The Moon passes Jupiter, Saturn and Mars.

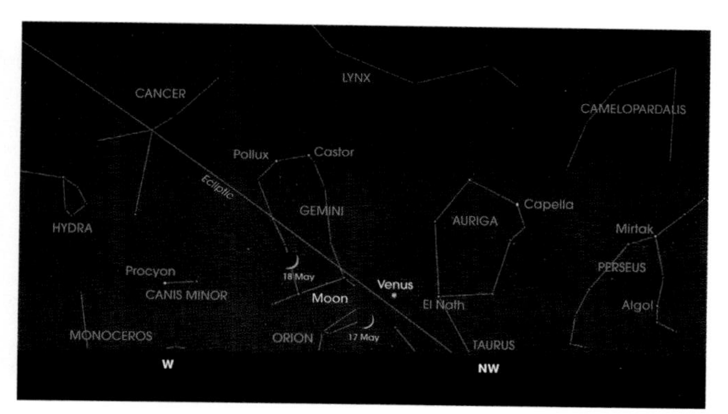

5b 17-18 May, 10.30 pm. Crescent Moon with Venus.

- **Venus** is the queen of the evening skies, blazing at magnitude −4.0 in the north-west and setting almost three hours after the Sun.
- Diametrically opposite around the horizon, in the south-east, the Evening Star has competition from **Jupiter**, at a glorious magnitude −2.5. The giant planet lies in the constellation of Libra, and is above the horizon all night long. Jupiter is at opposition on **9 May** (see Special Events). Use binoculars or a small telescope to spot its four largest moons.
- Next in the planetary line-up, **Saturn** rises in the south-east around midnight. At magnitude +0.3, the ringworld sits among the stars of Sagittarius.
- **Mars** begins the month in Sagittarius, but speeds into Capricornus by mid-May, brightening from magnitude −0.4 to −1.2. The Red Planet rises at about 2 am.

Mars

- Faint **Neptune** (magnitude +7.9) rises about 3 am, in Aquarius.
- **Mercury** and **Uranus** are lost in bright daylight in May.

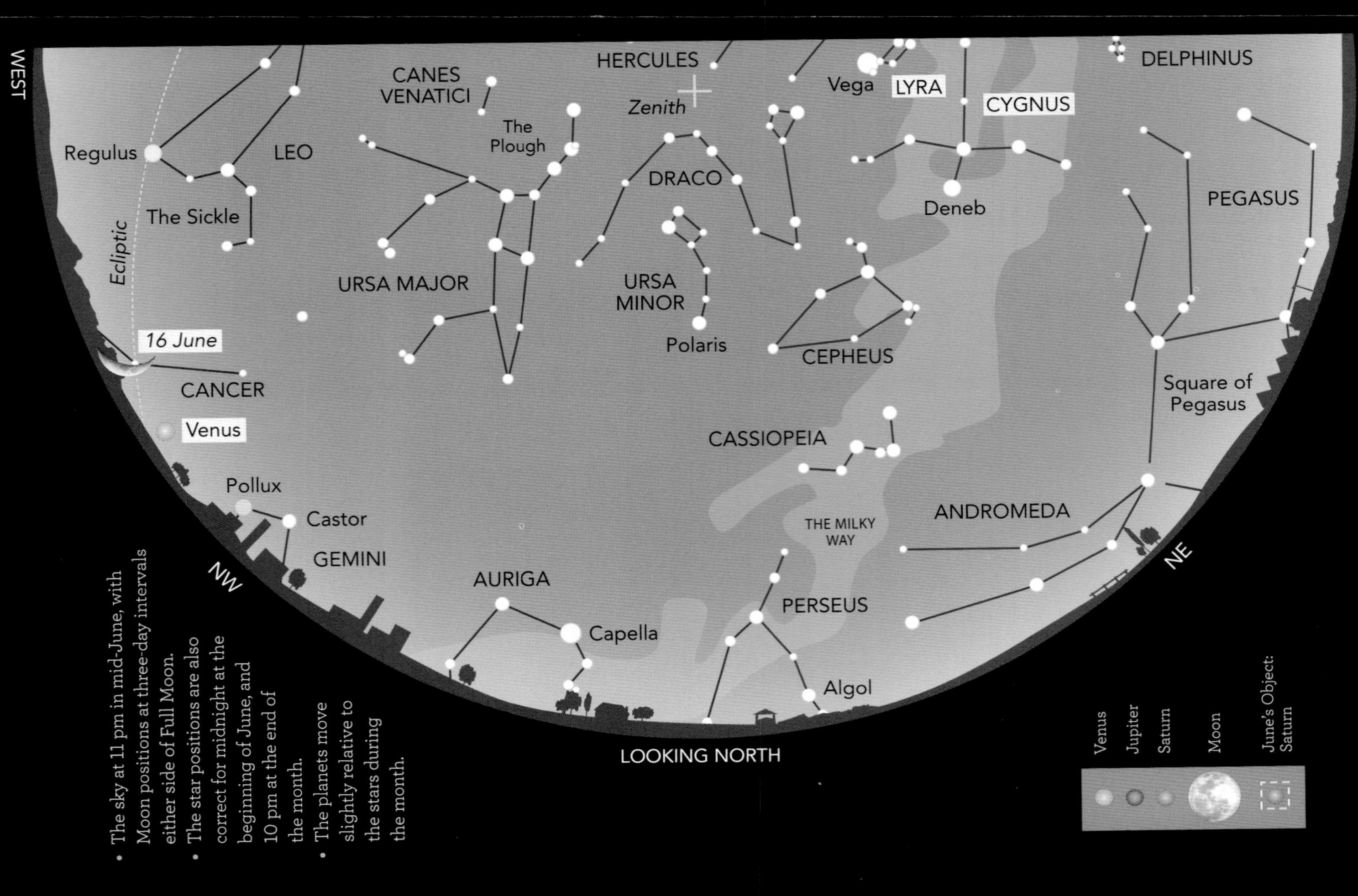

- The sky at 11 pm in mid-June, with Moon positions at three-day intervals either side of Full Moon.
- The star positions are also correct for midnight at the beginning of June, and 10 pm at the end of the month.
- The planets move slightly relative to the stars during the month.

JUNE

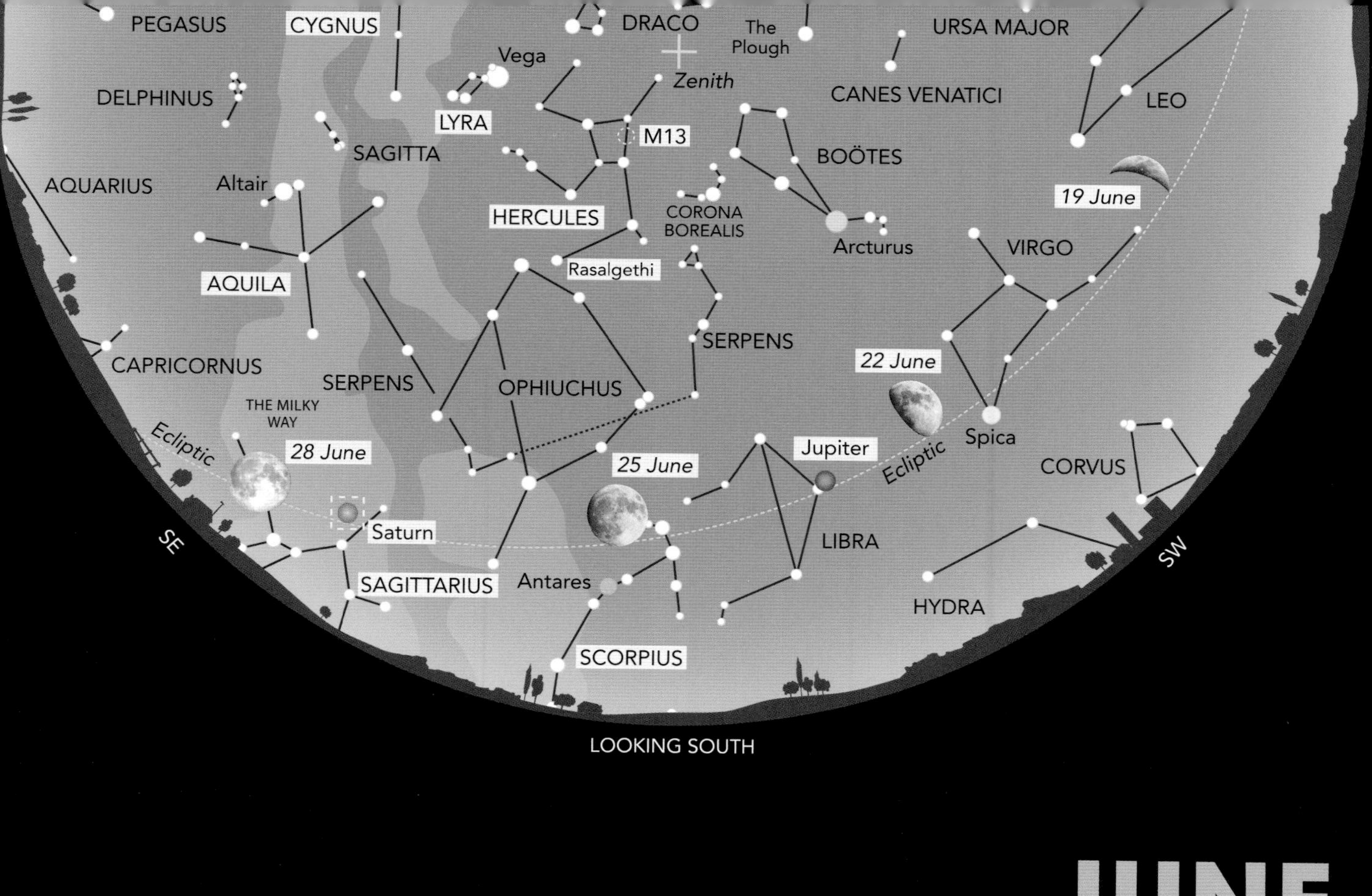

EAST
WEST
PEGASUS
CYGNUS
DRACO
The Plough
URSA MAJOR
Vega
Zenith
DELPHINUS
CANES VENATICI
LEO
LYRA
M13
SAGITTA
BOÖTES
AQUARIUS
Altair
19 June
HERCULES
CORONA BOREALIS
Arcturus
VIRGO
Rasalgethi
AQUILA
SERPENS
CAPRICORNUS
22 June
SERPENS
OPHIUCHUS
THE MILKY WAY
Spica
Ecliptic
28 June
Jupiter
Ecliptic
25 June
CORVUS
Saturn
SE
LIBRA
SAGITTARIUS
Antares
SW
HYDRA
SCORPIUS
LOOKING SOUTH

Venus and **Jupiter** are brilliant, despite skies that hardly grow dark for many of us in midsummer, and **Saturn** is putting on its best show of the year. It's not the best month for spotting faint stars, but take advantage of the soft, warm weather to acquaint yourself with the lovely summer constellations of **Hercules, Scorpius, Lyra, Cygnus** and **Aquila**.

JUNE'S CONSTELLATION

For one of antiquity's superheroes – famous for his 12 heroic labours – the celestial version of **Hercules** is a wimp. While Orion is all strutting masculinity in the winter sky, summer's Hercules is a poor reflection – and upside-down to boot.

Dig a little deeper, however, and you'll find a fascinating constellation. Below the hero's rectangular 'body' lies **Rasalgethi**, marking Hercules' head. About 400 times the Sun's girth, this giant star is flopping and billowing in its death throes, varying in brightness from third to fourth magnitude over a period of 90 days.

Hercules boasts one of the most spectacular sights in the northern night sky. Once the sky has grown really dark, look along the right-hand edge of its main rectangle for a fuzzy patch. **M13** is a bee-like swarm of a third of a million red giant stars, some of the oldest denizens of our Galaxy. One of the brightest 'globular clusters', it's really great in a small telescope (see April's Picture).

JUNE'S OBJECT

Saturn is at its closest this year, livening up the southern constellation of **Sagittarius** (the Archer). It's a glorious sight through a small telescope: the world looks surreal, like an exquisite model hanging in space.

The planet is famed for its huge engirdling appendages: its rings would stretch nearly all the way from the Earth to the Moon. The rings are made of myriad ice particles, and the Cassini spaceprobe found that some of them are clumping together into moonlets. And that's just the beginning of Saturn's larger family. It has at least 62 moons, including Titan (visible through a small telescope) which boasts lakes of liquid methane and ethane, and possibly active volcanoes. The icy moon Enceladus is spewing salty water into space, while Dione has traces of oxygen in its thin atmosphere. These discoveries raise the intriguing possibility of primitive life on Saturn's moons...

Saturn itself is second only to **Jupiter** in size. But its density is so low that – were you to plop it in an ocean – it would float. Saturn has a ferocious spin rate, turning once in 10 hours 32 minutes, and its winds roar at speeds of up to 1800 km/h.

JUNE'S TOPIC: WHAT IS A COMET?

Everyone is thrilled when a new comet hoves into view: over 20 years on, many people remember the magnificent Comet Hale-Bopp of 1997.

But comets have long had a dodgy reputation. Shakespeare wrote in *Julius Caesar*: 'When beggars die, there are no comets seen. The heavens themselves blaze forth the death of princes.' Resembling a malevolent cosmic dagger, a

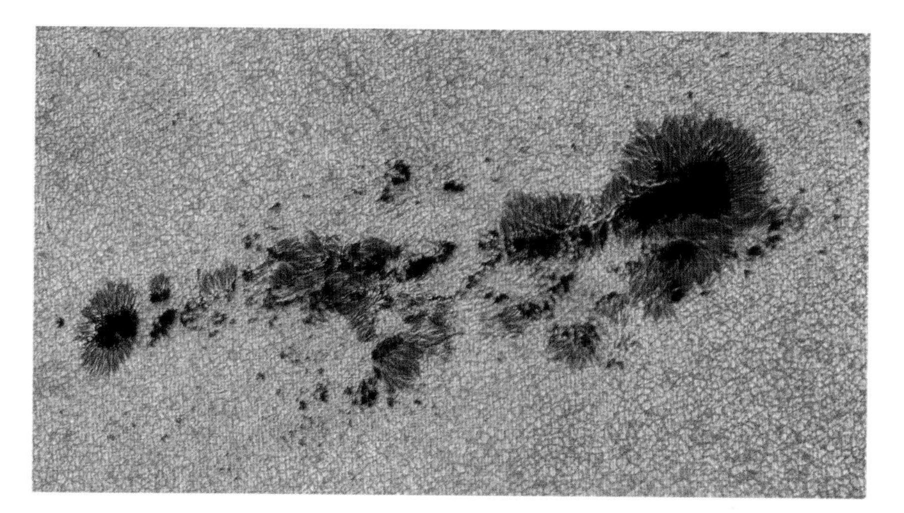

Damian Peach from Hamble, Hampshire, obtained this very high-resolution shot of a large sunspot on 6 July 2013 through his 355 mm C14 Schmidt-Cassegrain reflector. He used a video sequence of frames taken using a ZWO ASI174 camera.

comet was a portent of disaster. Indeed, about 65 million years ago, a comet (or a small asteroid) smashed into the Earth and destroyed the dinosaurs.

In reality, a comet is a 'dirty snowball', a lump of ice and rock left over from the creation of the planets. Comets reside in a vast region surrounding the Solar System, the **Oort-Öpik Cloud**, named after astronomers Jan Oort and Ernst Öpik who predicted it. Dislodged by a passing star, a comet may sweep in towards the Sun's heat, which boils away its ice into a vast head of gas and a tail millions of kilometres long. And yet these maligned visitors may actually be bearers of life, possibly delivering the ice that melted to become Earth's oceans – along with organic molecules.

OBSERVING TIP

June is *the* month for the best Sun-viewing, with the chance of picking up dark sunspots blotting its fair face. But be careful. NEVER look at the Sun directly, with your naked eyes or – especially – with a telescope or binoculars: it could well blind you permanently. Project the Sun's image through binoculars or a telescope onto a piece of white card. Or – if you want the real biz – get some solar binoculars or a solar telescope, with filters that guarantee a safe view. Check the web for details.

JUNE'S PICTURE

This staggering image of a giant sunspot group covers an area 11 times wider than the Earth! It's a complex of magnetic fields, confining the Sun's brilliant roiling gases. This spot was a last gasp in the 11-year cycle of solar activity that's just finished. Having lasted for three revolutions of the Sun in 2013, the spot complex produced an enormous flare on 12 July. Astronomers are now looking forward the next solar maximum: the spots should start arriving in 2019.

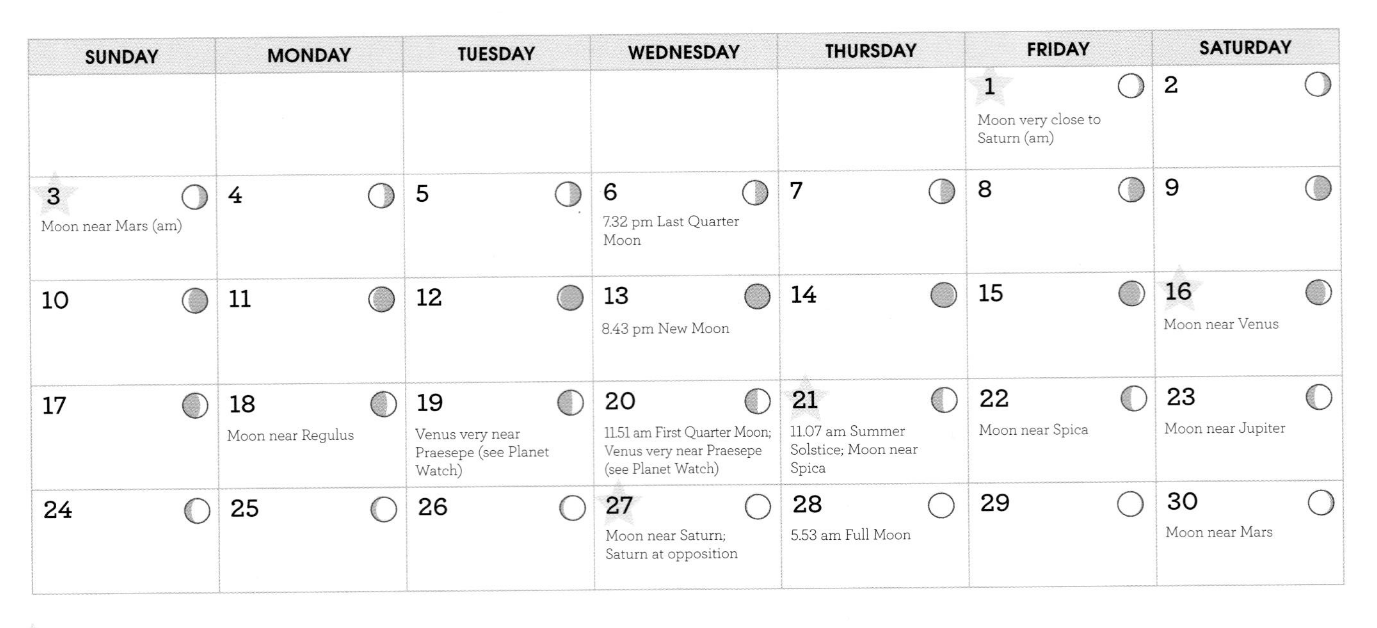

SUNDAY	MONDAY	TUESDAY	WEDNESDAY	THURSDAY	FRIDAY	SATURDAY
					1 Moon very close to Saturn (am)	2
3 Moon near Mars (am)	4	5	6 7.32 pm Last Quarter Moon	7	8	9
10	11	12	13 8.43 pm New Moon	14	15	16 Moon near Venus
17	18 Moon near Regulus	19 Venus very near Praesepe (see Planet Watch)	20 11.51 am First Quarter Moon; Venus very near Praesepe (see Planet Watch)	21 11.07 am Summer Solstice; Moon near Spica	22 Moon near Spica	23 Moon near Jupiter
24	25	26	27 Moon near Saturn; Saturn at opposition	28 5.53 am Full Moon	29	30 Moon near Mars

SPECIAL EVENTS

- **1, 3 June:** the Moon passes Saturn and Mars in the morning sky (Chart 6a).
- **16 June:** Low in the western sky after sunset, the crescent Moon forms a striking spectacle with Venus. With binoculars, you'll find Praesepe (the Beehive star cluster) just above the Moon.
- **21 June, 11.07 am:** Summer Solstice. The Sun reaches its most northerly point in the sky, so 21 June is Midsummer's Day, with the longest period of daylight and the shortest night.
- **27 June:** Saturn is opposite to the Sun in the sky and at its closest to Earth this year, 1354 million km away (see Planet Watch and this month's Object).

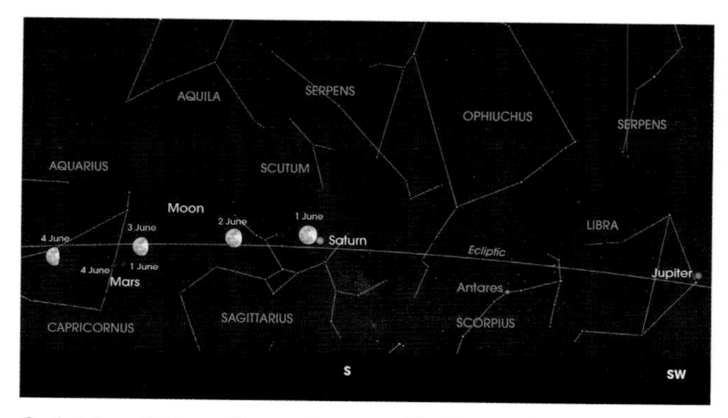

6a 1–4 June, 2.30 am. Close conjunction of the Moon and Saturn; also Jupiter and Mars.

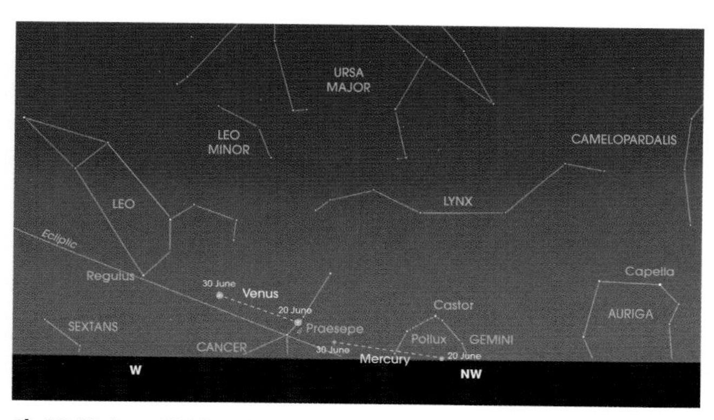

6b 20–30 June, 10.30 pm. Venus, Praesepe and Mercury.

- We have a glorious Evening Star livening up our summer nights: it's the planet **Venus**, shining at magnitude –4.0 in the west after sunset, and staying above the horizon almost until midnight. On **11 June**, Venus is in line with the twin stars Castor and Pollux. Check out the brilliant planet on **19 and 20 June** with binoculars or a small telescope, and you'll see it's almost in front of the Beehive star cluster, Praesepe (Chart 6b).
- Toward the end of June, Venus is joined by its little brother **Mercury**: you'll find the innermost planet to the lower right of the Evening Star, around 30 times fainter at magnitude –0.3 (Chart 6b). On **27 June**, Mercury is in line with Castor and Pollux, which are about quarter its brightness (best seen with binoculars).
- The brilliant 'star' in the southern sky is giant planet **Jupiter**, lording it over Libra at magnitude –2.4. It sets around 3 am.
- **Saturn** is at opposition this month (see Special Events and this month's Object). The ringworld lies above the horizon all night long, shining in Sagittarius at magnitude 0.0. Use a small telescope to spot its famous rings and brightest moon, Titan.
- **Mars** lies in Capricornus, brightening from magnitude –1.2 to –2.2 during June. It rises about midnight.
- Dim **Neptune** lurks in Aquarius: at magnitude +7.9, it rises around 1 am. Following behind, **Uranus** (magnitude +5.9) is rising about 2.30 am on the border of Aries and Pisces.

- The sky at 11 pm in mid-July, with Moon positions at three-day intervals either side of Full Moon.
- The star positions are also correct for midnight at the beginning of July, and 10 pm at the end of the month.
- The planets move slightly relative to the stars during the month.

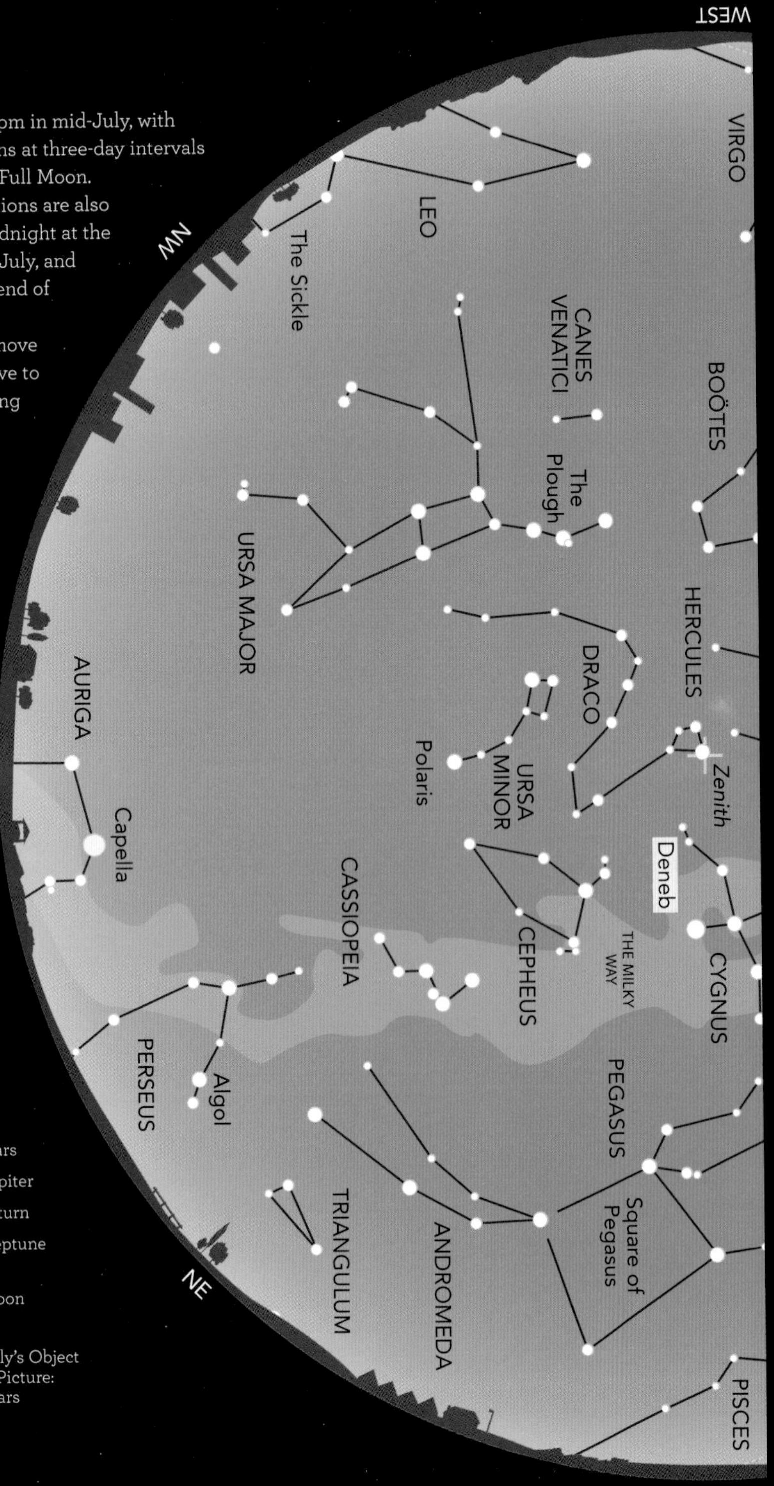

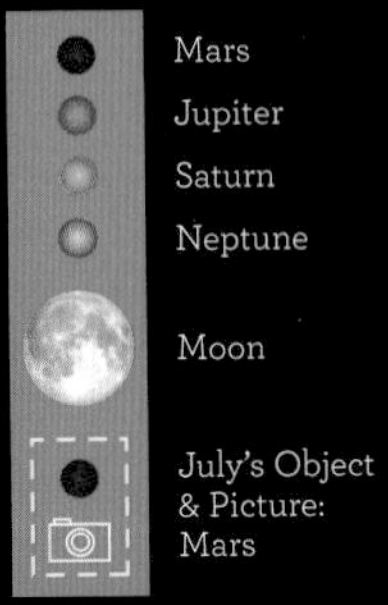

Mars
Jupiter
Saturn
Neptune
Moon
July's Object & Picture: Mars

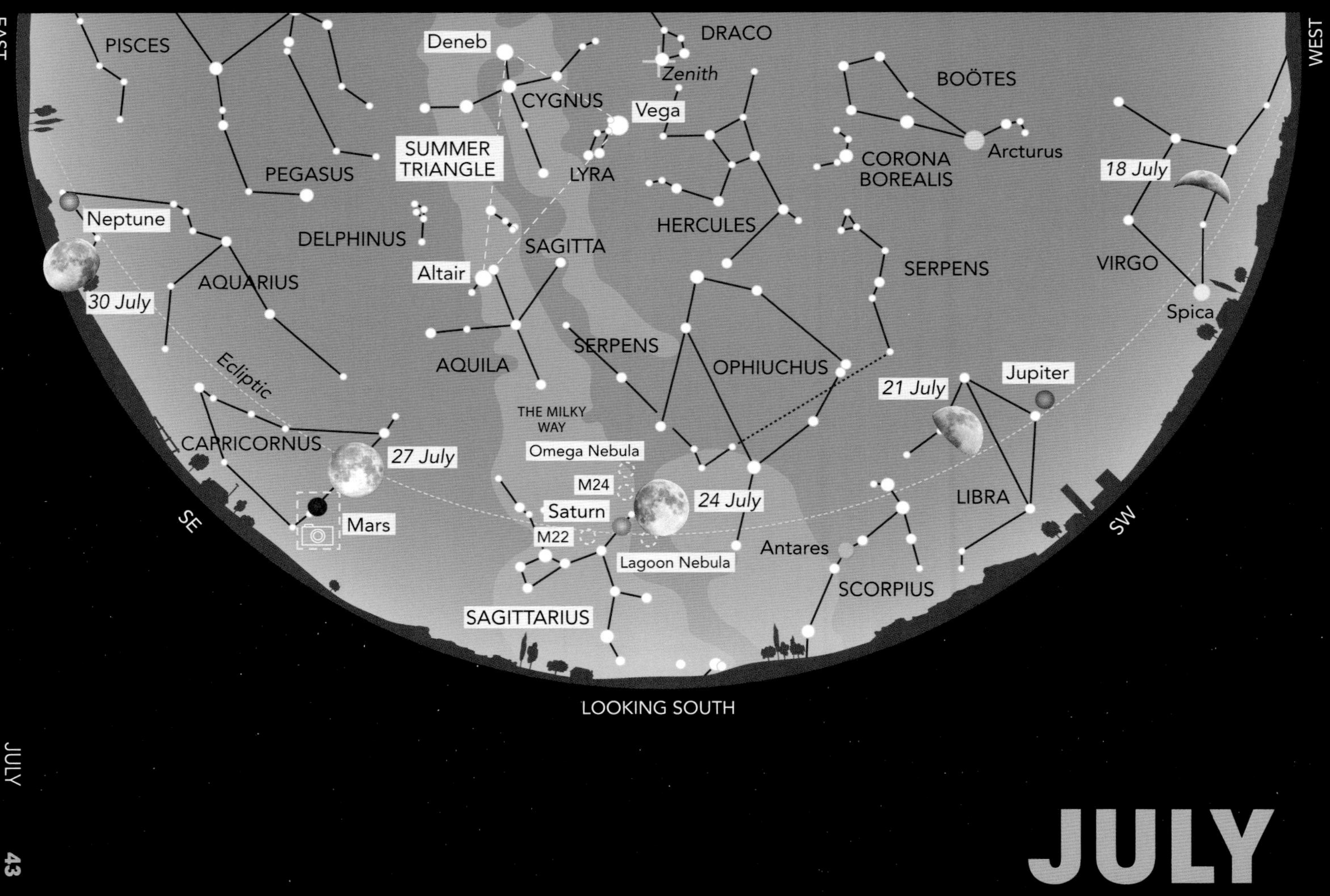
EAST
WEST
PISCES
Deneb
DRACO
Zenith
BOÖTES
CYGNUS
Vega
SUMMER TRIANGLE
PEGASUS
LYRA
CORONA BOREALIS
Arcturus
18 July
Neptune
DELPHINUS
HERCULES
SAGITTA
Altair
AQUARIUS
SERPENS
VIRGO
30 July
Spica
AQUILA
SERPENS
OPHIUCHUS
Ecliptic
Jupiter
21 July
THE MILKY WAY
Omega Nebula
CAPRICORNUS
27 July
M24
24 July
LIBRA
Saturn
SE
Mars
M22
Lagoon Nebula
Antares
SW
SCORPIUS
SAGITTARIUS
LOOKING SOUTH
JULY

Mars has the starring role, a brilliant ochre-red gem low down in **Sagittarius**, surrounded by jewels of the Milky Way. Along with **Venus** and **Jupiter**, we have three planets on display that are brighter than any star: counting in fainter Mercury and Saturn, there's a rare chance to catch all the naked-eye planets in the same evening. We're also treated to glorious stars such as **Vega**, **Deneb** and **Altair**, which comprise the **Summer Triangle**.

JULY'S CONSTELLATION

Low down in the south, you'll find a constellation that's shaped rather like a teapot, with the handle to the left and the spout to the right.

To the ancient Greeks, the star pattern of **Sagittarius** represented an archer, with the torso of a man and the body of a horse. The 'handle' of the teapot represents his upper body; the curve of three stars to the right his bent bow, while the end of the spout is the point of the arrow, aimed at Scorpius, the fearsome celestial scorpion.

Sagittarius is rich in nebulae and star clusters. If you have a clear night (and preferably from a southern latitude), sweep Sagittarius with binoculars for some fantastic sights. Above the spout lies the wonderful **Lagoon Nebula** – a region of starbirth that's visible to the naked eye on clear nights. Between Sagittarius and Aquila, you'll find a bright patch of stars in the Milky Way, catalogued as **M24**. Raise your binoculars higher to spot another star-forming region, the **Omega Nebula**.

Finally, on a very dark night you may spot a fuzzy patch, above and to the left of the teapot's lid. This is the globular cluster **M22**, a swarm of almost a million stars that lies 10,600 light years away.

OBSERVING TIP

This is the month when you really need a good, unobstructed horizon to the south, for the best views of the glorious summer constellations of Scorpius and Sagittarius. They never rise high in temperate latitudes, so make the best of a southerly view – especially over the sea – if you're away on holiday. A good southern horizon is also best for views of the planets, because they rise highest when they're in the south.

JULY'S OBJECT

Mars – now at its closest to Earth – is the second smallest planet in the Solar System, and the world most similar to our own. The Red Planet has polar caps, huge exposures of dark rocks, an atmosphere (very thin, and mainly carbon dioxide), seasons (twice as long as ours, because of Mars's distance from the Sun), and even clouds.

But what's most astonishing about Mars is its geology. All the extremes in the Solar System are here. The planet boasts an enormous canyon, Valles Marineris, which is 4000 kilometres long and 7 kilometres deep. This enormous crack was caused by the upwelling of the Tharsis Ridge, home to a family of vast volcanoes. Although not active today, it's just possible that they're dormant and could erupt tomorrow.

Largest of the volcanoes – and biggest in the Solar System – is Olympus Mons. At 26km, the volcano is three times higher than Mt Everest. It would completely cover England, and its central crater could swallow London.

JULY'S TOPIC: THE SEARCH FOR EXTRA-TERRESTRIAL INTELLIGENCE

It's the biggest question in astronomy: is there anybody out there? It's now half a century since American astronomer Frank Drake turned his radio telescope to the heavens in the hope of hearing an alien broadcast. Despite false alarms, there has been a deafening silence.

Drake and his colleagues founded the SETI Institute (Search for Extra-Terrestrial Intelligence), which investigates all aspects of communicating with alien life. Thanks to a donation from Microsoft co-founder Paul Allen, the team is now building an array of 350 radio telescopes in California to tune into that first whisper from ET.

Many leading radio telescopes – from Australia to the UK – 'do' SETI when their scientific programmes allow. Amateur researchers are also searching: members of the project SETI.net have built their own radio telescope. Too much? Use your computer's down time to analyse data from the Big Guys, and you could discover *the signal.* Details from SETI@home

But is life out there far more advanced than us? Is radio communication something that came and went? The SETI researchers are contemplating communication by laser beams. Others are looking for 'technosignatures', unnatural activity on distant planets that could range from city lights to forest fires.

JULY'S PICTURE

Even a moderate telescope can reveal Mars's complex topography. At the bottom of the picture is the *northern* polar cap (telescopes invert the image to avoid having extra light-draining optics). The markings on the left-hand side of the disc are exposures of dark rock, contrasting with the dusty red deserts. The clouds to the right overlie the Tharsis Bulge and its gigantic volcanoes, with mighty Olympus Mons at extreme right.

Damian Peach captured this image on 12 April 2014, when he took his Celestron C14 reflector to Barbados: the planet was 15 arcseconds in diameter. He used a ZWO ASI120MM camera to take separate video sequences through red, green and blue filters. (You can see the complete video at http://www.damianpeach.com/mars1314.htm)

SUNDAY	MONDAY	TUESDAY	WEDNESDAY	THURSDAY	FRIDAY	SATURDAY
1 Moon near Mars	2	3	4	5	6 8.51 am Last Quarter Moon; 5.47 pm Earth at aphelion	7
8	9 Venus very close to Regulus (see Planet Watch)	10	11	12 Mercury greatest eastern elongation	13 3.48 am New Moon; partial solar eclipse	14 Moon near Mercury (see Planet Watch)
15 Moon between Venus and Regulus (see Planet Watch)	16	17	18	19 8.52 pm First Quarter Moon; Moon near Spica	20 Moon near Jupiter (Chart 7b)	21
22 Moon near Antares (Chart 7b)	23	24 Moon near Saturn (Chart 7b)	25	26	27 Mars opposition; Moon near Mars (Chart 7b); 9.21 pm Full Moon; total lunar eclipse	28
29	30	31				

SPECIAL EVENTS

- **6 July:** the Earth reaches aphelion, its furthest point from the Sun – 152 million km.
- **13 July:** the southernmost regions of Australia and New Zealand witness a partial eclipse of the Sun; it's not visible from the UK.
- **27 July:** Mars is opposite to the Sun in the sky; because the planet's orbit is not circular, it is closest to Earth – 57.6 million km away – four days later (see Planet Watch and this month's Object).
- **27 July:** a total eclipse of the Moon is visible from Africa, Europe and western Asia. As seen from Britain, the Moon rises totally eclipsed in the south-east around 9 pm, appearing as a dim coppery globe directly above brilliant red Mars; the Moon starts to reappear about 10.15 pm.
- This month, Japan's Hayabusa 2 spaceprobe reaches asteroid Ryugu. It will drop landers and collect samples of the asteroid's rocks that it will return to Earth.
- NASA plans to launch Solar Probe Plus, to study the Sun in close-up, in late July or August.

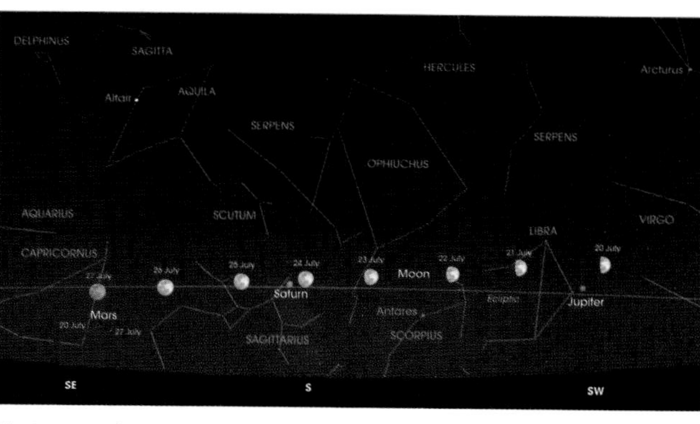

7a *9–16 July, 10 pm. Venus with Regulus and the crescent Moon.*

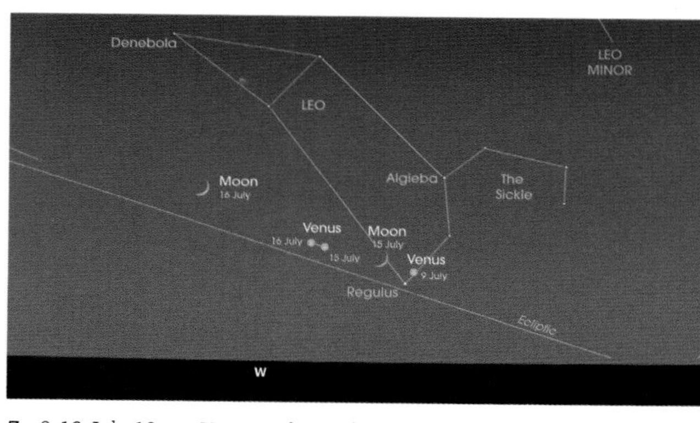

7b *20–27 July, 10.30 pm. Moon with Jupiter, Saturn and Mars; total lunar eclipse.*

• **Venus** is lighting up the north-western sky after sunset at magnitude –4.1. At the start of July, the brilliant Evening Star is setting 2 hours after the Sun, but it's gradually slipping down into the dusk glow. On **9 July**, Venus passes just above Regulus, while it forms a stunning tableau with the crescent Moon and Regulus on **15 July** (Chart 7a).

• At the beginning of July, you may spot **Mercury** skulking very low in the evening twilight to the lower right of Venus and setting just over an hour after the Sun. But the innermost planet quickly fades from its initial magnitude of 0.0 and is lost in the twilight by mid-month.

• Giant planet **Jupiter** is glorious in the southern sky, shining at magnitude –2.2 in Libra, and setting about 1 am. In the south-east, you'll find dimmer **Saturn** (magnitude +0.1) nestled among the stars of Sagittarius. The ringworld sinks below the horizon just before 4 am.

• **Mars** is barnstorming into view in Capricornus, rising at 11.15 pm at the beginning of July and 9.15 pm by month's end. It reaches opposition on **27 July** (see Special Events) and closest approach on **31 July**, when the Red Planet outshines even Jupiter, at magnitude –2.8.

• Dim and distant **Neptune** lies in Aquarius: at magnitude +7.8, it rises around 11 pm. It's followed by **Uranus** (magnitude +5.8), which rises in Aries just after midnight.

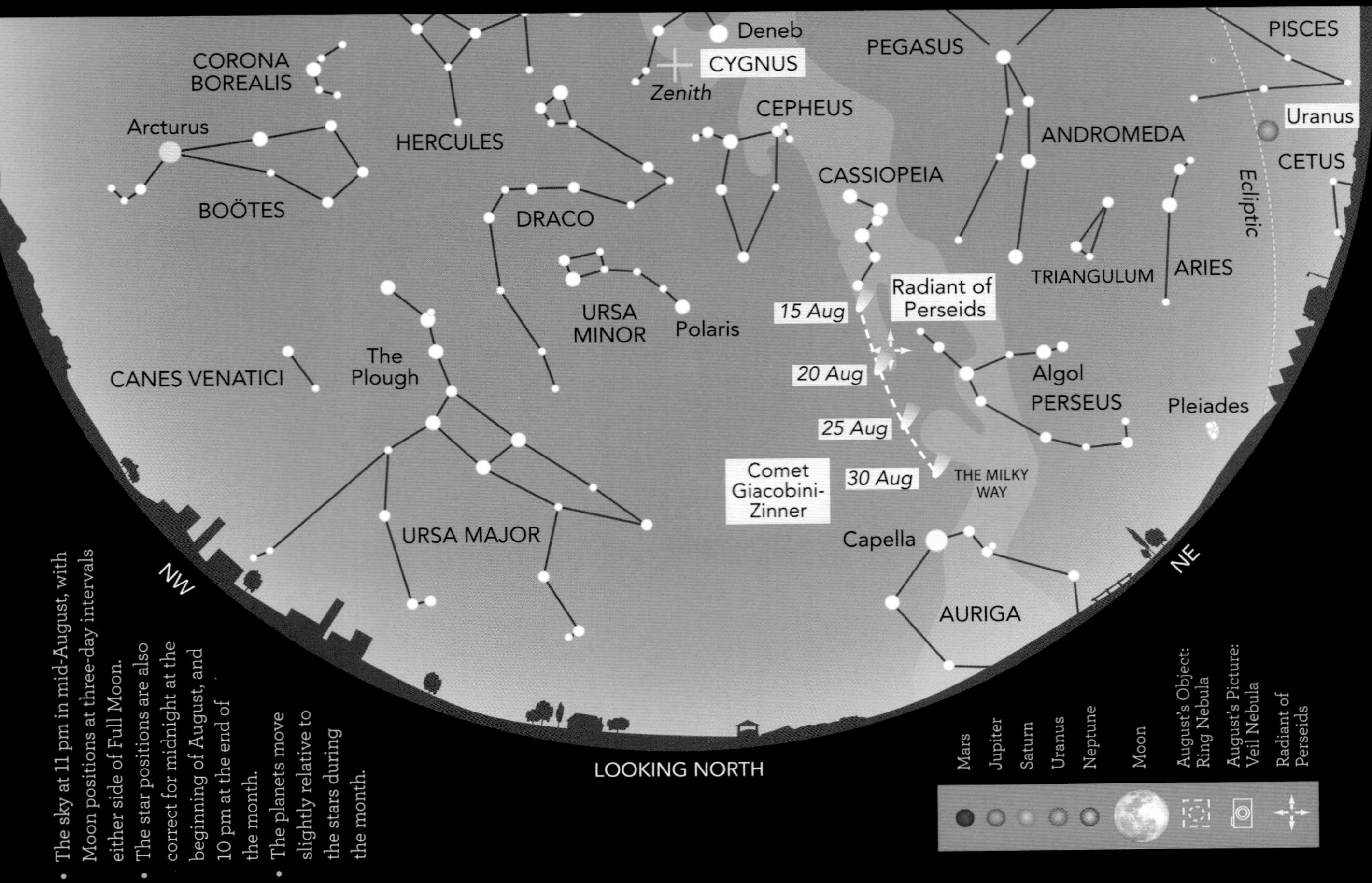

- The sky at 11 pm in mid-August, with Moon positions at three-day intervals either side of Full Moon.
- The star positions are also correct for midnight at the beginning of August, and 10 pm at the end of the month.
- The planets move slightly relative to the stars during the month.

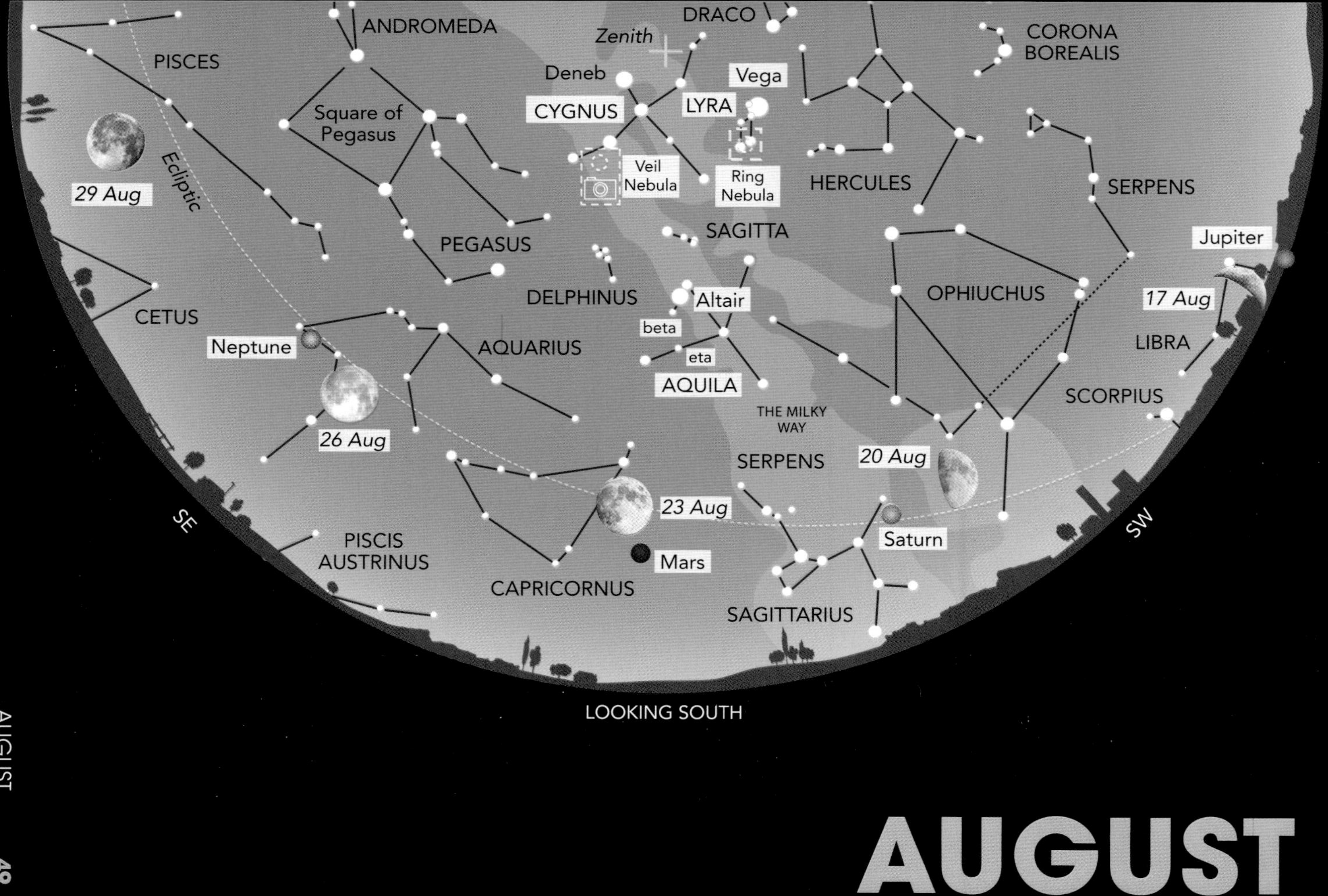
EAST
WEST
ANDROMEDA
DRACO
Zenith
CORONA BOREALIS
PISCES
Deneb
Vega
CYGNUS
LYRA
Square of Pegasus
29 Aug
Ecliptic
Veil Nebula
Ring Nebula
HERCULES
SERPENS
SAGITTA
PEGASUS
Jupiter
DELPHINUS
Altair
OPHIUCHUS
17 Aug
CETUS
beta
Neptune
AQUARIUS
eta
LIBRA
AQUILA
SCORPIUS
THE MILKY WAY
26 Aug
SERPENS
20 Aug
23 Aug
SE
Saturn
SW
PISCIS AUSTRINUS
Mars
CAPRICORNUS
SAGITTARIUS
LOOKING SOUTH

AUGUST

A picturesque parade of planets stretches across the southern sky in the early evening, from beautiful Venus in the west, through giant **Jupiter** and duller **Saturn** to the glorious Red Planet, **Mars**. And we're treated to celestial fireworks, with the sensational **Perseid** meteor shower.

AUGUST'S CONSTELLATION

It has to be admitted that **Aquila** does vaguely resemble a flying eagle, albeit a rather faint one. It's an ancient constellation, named after the bird that was a companion to the god Jupiter – and even carried his thunderbolts for him!

The constellation is dominated by **Altair**, a young blue-white star 17 light years away, which is 11 times brighter than our Sun. It has a very fast spin: the star hurtles around at 210 kilometres per second, rotating in just 9 hours (as opposed to about 30 days for the Sun). As a result, it is oval in shape. Altair is a triple star, as is its neighbour **beta Aquilae** (just below, left). **Eta Aquilae** (immediately below beta) is one of the brightest Cepheid variable stars – old stars that change their brightness by swelling and shrinking. The pulsations of eta Aquilae make it vary from magnitude +3.5 to +4.4 every seven days.

AUGUST'S OBJECT

Tucked into the small constellation of **Lyra** (the Lyre) – near brilliant **Vega** – lies a strange celestial sight. It was first spotted by French astronomer Antoine Darquier in 1779 as: 'a very dull nebula, but perfectly outlined; as large as Jupiter and looks like a fading planet'.

You can see this object with even a small telescope, though a magnification of 50 is needed to distinguish it from a star: you'll then make out the distinctive shape that gives it the name the **Ring Nebula**.

Like other planetary nebulae (named for their appearance), it's the expanding remains of an old star, lit up by the original star's incandescent core. The Ring Nebula is a barrel-shaped bubble of gas that we happen to view end-on. Aliens observing the Ring Nebula from another perspective would undoubtedly call it something different!

AUGUST'S TOPIC: METEOR SHOWERS

So many people report to us that they see loads of shooting stars on their summer holidays and are amazed when

OBSERVING TIP

Hold a 'meteor party' to check out the spectacular Perseid meteor shower on 12/13 August. You don't need any optical equipment – in fact, telescopes and binoculars will restrict your view of the shooting stars, which can appear anywhere. The ideal viewing equipment is your unaided eye, plus a warm sleeping bag and a lounger. Everyone should look in different directions, so you can cover the whole sky: shout out 'Meteor!' when you see a shooting star. One of the party can record the observations, using a watch, notepad and red torch. In the interests of science, try to observe the sky for at least an hour, before repairing indoors for some meteoric celebrations...

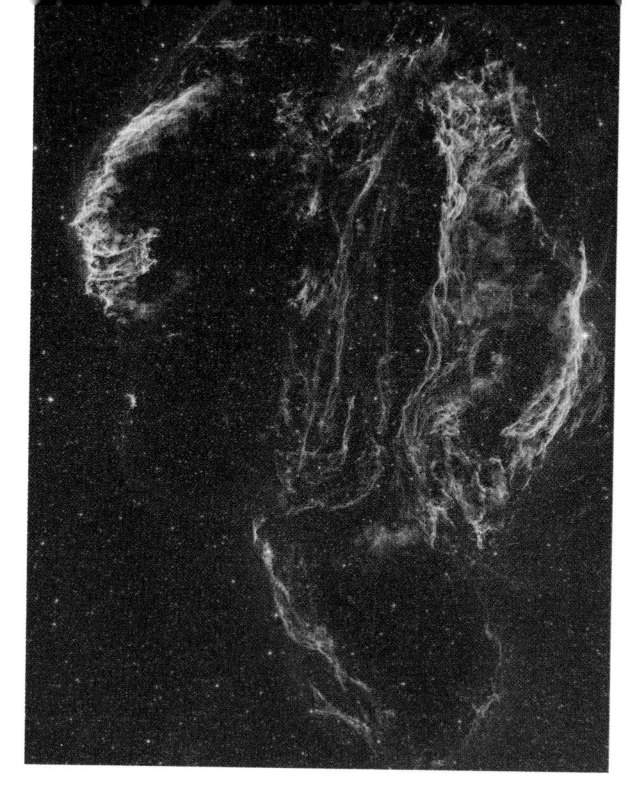

In the dark skies of Olocau in Spain, Sara Wager used a Takahashi 85 mm refractor with a 0.73 focal reducer to give the wide field of view needed for this image of the Veil Nebula, combining two panes to show its full extent. For each pane she gave 15 half-hour exposures through both hydrogen-alpha and OIII filters on a QSI 683 camera.

we comment, 'So you go on holiday in August?' This month each year the Earth runs into a stream of debris from Comet Swift-Tuttle, which burns up as the **Perseid meteor shower** (see Special Events).

It's not the only regular shower of shooting stars. We run into several dusty trails from comets and asteroids during the year, giving us about a dozen good meteor showers when you might get to see 50–60 meteors an hour. They include the Orionids (October), the Leonids (November), and the Geminids (December). (All the details are given under Special Events for the relevant month.)

Meteors are notoriously unpredictable. We may encounter a dense knot in the stream of debris, and – hey presto – thousands of meteors. Most sensational was the storm over America in 1833, when the Leonids streamed down at 100,000 an hour!

So go out and stargaze when a meteor shower is due. You never know what's on offer...

AUGUST'S PICTURE

At six times the size of the Moon, the **Veil Nebula** (in the constellation **Cygnus**) is the largest supernova remnant in the northern sky. Discovered by William Herschel in 1784, its distance has recently been revised downwards, from 2500 years to 1470 light years, meaning the nebula is 90 light years across. Also known as the Cygnus Loop, these glowing gas clouds have been swept up by shock waves from a supernova that exploded 5000–8000 years ago. As the shock front expands, the appearance of the nebula is constantly changing.

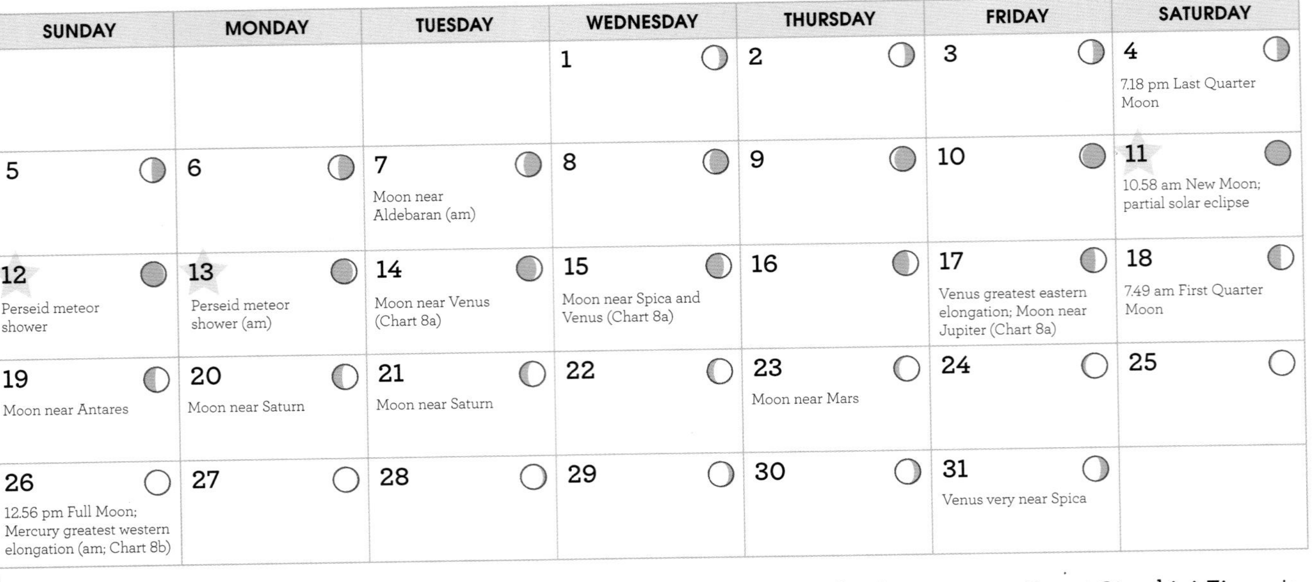

SUNDAY	MONDAY	TUESDAY	WEDNESDAY	THURSDAY	FRIDAY	SATURDAY
			1	2	3	4 7.18 pm Last Quarter Moon
5	6	7 Moon near Aldebaran (am)	8	9	10	11 10.58 am New Moon; partial solar eclipse
12 Perseid meteor shower	13 Perseid meteor shower (am)	14 Moon near Venus (Chart 8a)	15 Moon near Spica and Venus (Chart 8a)	16	17 Venus greatest eastern elongation; Moon near Jupiter (Chart 8a)	18 7.49 am First Quarter Moon
19 Moon near Antares	20 Moon near Saturn	21 Moon near Saturn	22	23 Moon near Mars	24	25
26 12.56 pm Full Moon; Mercury greatest western elongation (am; Chart 8b)	27	28	29	30	31 Venus very near Spica	

SPECIAL EVENTS

- **11 August:** a partial eclipse of the Sun can be seen from northern Europe, north-east Canada and north-east Asia. People in the very north of the Scotland mainland, Orkney and Shetland will see a tiny chunk taken out of the Sun around 9.50 am. **Do not observe the sun directly: use one of the safe methods given in June's observing tip.**
- **Night of 12/13 August:** maximum of the **Perseid** meteor shower, when the Earth runs into debris from Comet Swift-Tuttle. This year is ideal for observing Perseids in a dark sky as the Moon is out of the way.
- This month, NASA's OSIRIS-REx mission reaches asteroid Bennu. It will scoop up a sample of the surface and return it to Earth for analysis.
- **Comet Giacobini-Zinner** is visible through binoculars in the latter half of August (see this month's Star Chart). It's predicted to reach magnitude +7.0 by the end of the month – though comets are so fickle that it may flare to become visible to the naked eye.

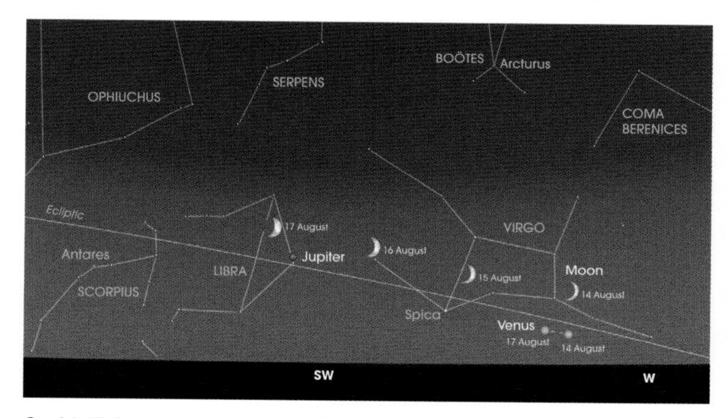

8a 14–17 August, 9 pm. Moon with Venus and Jupiter.

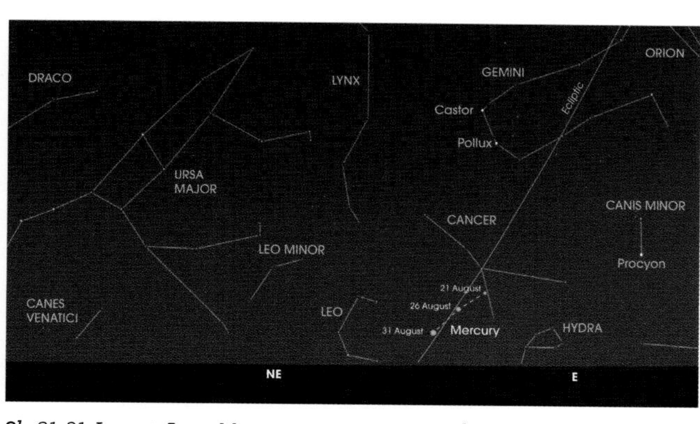

8b 21–31 August, 5 am. Mercury greatest western elongation.

• Over the past few months, the Evening Star has been a familiar sight after sunset. But now brilliant **Venus** (magnitude –4.3) is sinking down into the western twilight, setting at 10.15 pm at the beginning of August but as early as 8.45 pm by the end of the month. You'll find Venus getting chummy with the crescent Moon on 14 August (Chart 8a), and with Spica on **31 August**.

• **Jupiter**, in the south-west in Libra, is fainter than Venus at magnitude –2.0, but appears just as prominent because we see it in a dark sky. The giant planet is setting around 11 pm. Mid-month, it lies close to a double star, the wonderfully named Zubenelgenubi ('southern claw').

• Further to the left, you'll find **Saturn** (magnitude +0.3) to the south in Sagittarius, setting about 1.30 am.

• Last in the line of bright planets stretching over the southern skies, **Mars** lies to the south-east, enlivening the dull constellation of Capricornus. It sets around 3 am. At the start of August, the Red Planet blazes at magnitude –2.7; but fades to –2.1 by the end of the month, as the faster-moving Earth pulls away from Mars.

• **Neptune** (magnitude +7.8) inhabits Aquarius, rising about 9 pm. It's followed by **Uranus** which rises around 10.30 pm and shines at magnitude +5.8 in Aries.

• Towards the end of August, early birds may spot **Mercury**, very low in the eastern dawn twilight about 5 am. Between **21 and 31 August**, it brightens dramatically from magnitude +1.0 to –0.7. From Chart 8b, spot the brighter stars while the sky is dark, and use them to locate Mercury when it rises.

- The sky at 11 pm in mid-September, with Moon positions at three-day intervals either side of Full Moon.
- The star positions are also correct for midnight at the beginning of September, and 10 pm at the end of the month.
- The planets move slightly relative to the stars during the month.

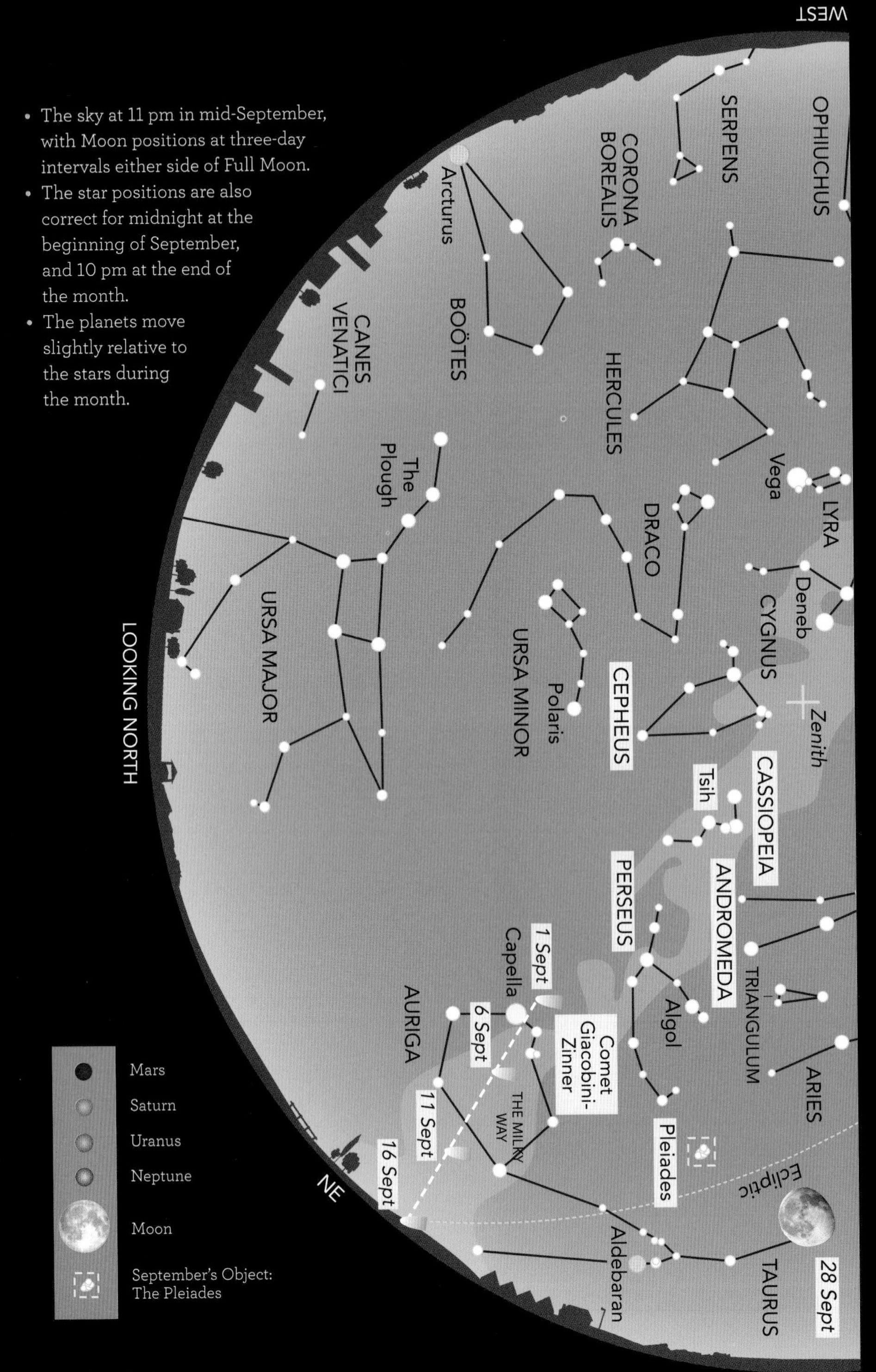

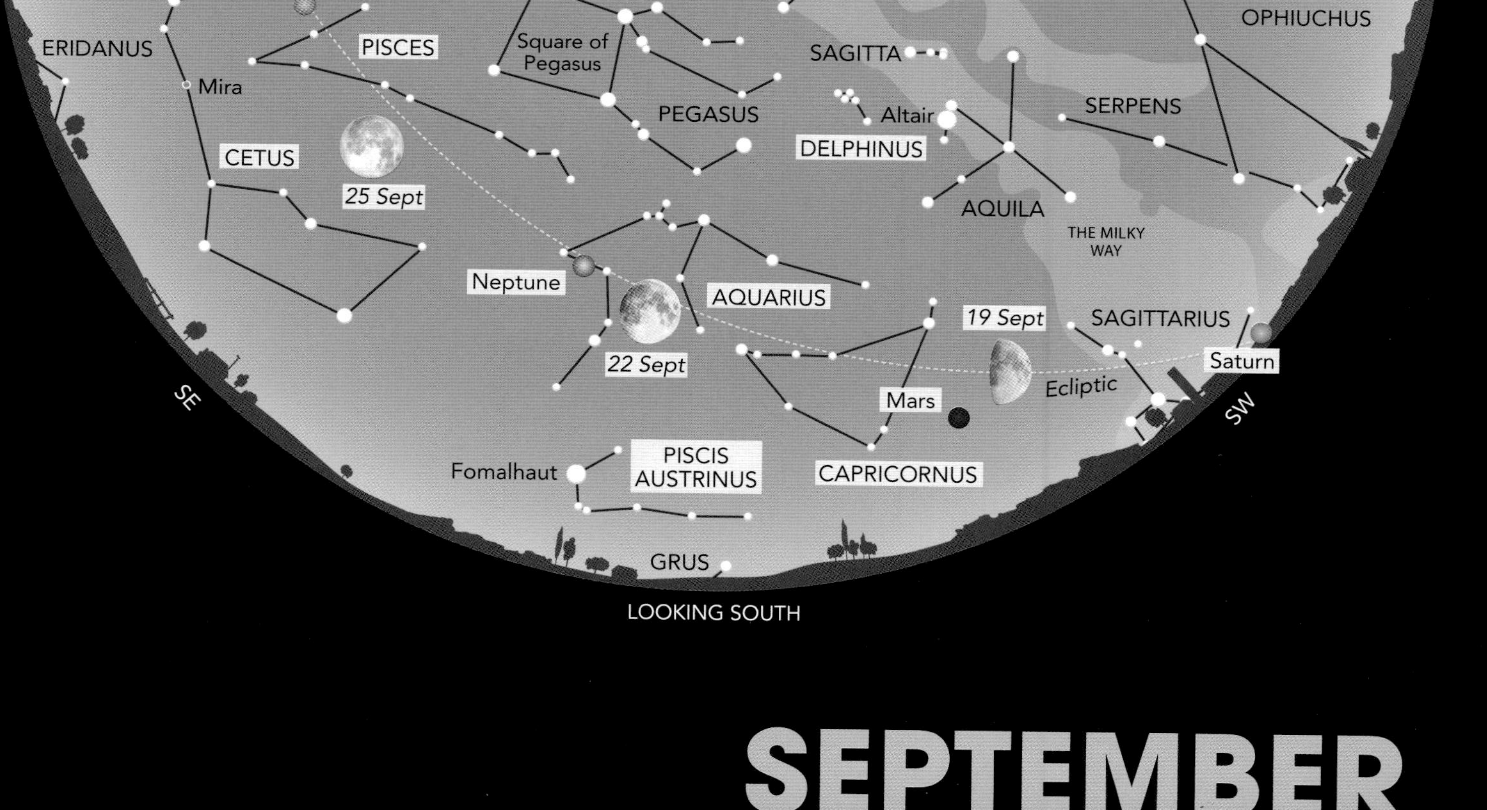
EAST
TAURUS
28 Sept
ARIES
TRIANGULUM
CEPHEUS
Zenith
ANDROMEDA
Deneb
CYGNUS
Vega
LYRA
HERCULES
SERPENS
WEST
Uranus
ERIDANUS
Mira
PISCES
Square of Pegasus
SAGITTA
OPHIUCHUS
PEGASUS
Altair
DELPHINUS
SERPENS
CETUS
25 Sept
AQUILA
THE MILKY WAY
Neptune
AQUARIUS
19 Sept
SAGITTARIUS
22 Sept
Saturn
Mars
Ecliptic
SE
SW
Fomalhaut
PISCIS AUSTRINUS
CAPRICORNUS
GRUS
LOOKING SOUTH

SEPTEMBER

The summer's brilliant pageant of planets is now tarnishing, as Venus exits the stage and Mars continues to fade. The sky is filling with the dim watery constellations of autumn: **Aquarius** (the Water Carrier), **Cetus** (the Sea Monster), **Capricornus** (the Sea Goat), **Pisces** (the Fishes), **Piscis Austrinus** (the Southern Fish) and **Delphinus** (the Dolphin). And – binoculars out for **Comet Giacobini-Zinner**.

SEPTEMBER'S CONSTELLATION

Look almost overhead for a star pattern in the unmistakable shape of a 'W'. To the ancients, this constellation represented Queen **Cassiopeia** of Ethiopia, who ruled with her husband King **Cepheus**.

Cassiopeia misguidedly boasted that her daughter **Andromeda** was more beautiful than the sea nymphs. The sea god, Poseidon, was so incensed that he sent a ravaging monster (**Cetus**) to eat the young people of the country. It could only be appeased by the sacrifice of Andromeda – but she was rescued by the hero **Perseus**. These five major players are now all immortalised in the heavens.

Unusually, the central star in Cassiopeia is known by its Chinese name – **Tsih** ('the whip'). This unstable star – some 55,000 times brighter than the Sun – is spinning around at breakneck pace, flinging out streams of gas.

Cassiopeia has experienced two supernovae, where an entire star has blown apart: one was seen by Danish astronomer Tycho Brahe in 1572, while the fireball from a second supernova (around 1660) is now the most prominent radio source in the sky, Cassiopeia A.

SEPTEMBER'S OBJECT

The **Pleiades** star cluster is one of the most familiar celestial objects. It is a lovely sight to the naked eye or through binoculars, and magnificent in a long-exposure image.

Though the cluster is well known as the Seven Sisters, skywatchers typically see any number of stars but seven! Most people can pick out the six brightest stars, while very keen-sighted observers can discern up to 11 members. These are just the most luminous in a group of at least 1000 stars, lying 444 light years away. The brightest stars in the Pleiades are hot and blue, and all the stars are young – around 100 million years old (about 2 per cent of the Sun's age).

The space observatory Spitzer has detected a disc around one of the Pleiades' stars. The hot money is that it's a planetary system in formation.

SEPTEMBER'S TOPIC: THE MOON'S CRATERS

Even binoculars show you that the Moon is covered in craters, first spotted by Galileo. In 1651, Giovanni Battista Riccioli gave names to 247 craters, immortalising eminent scientists and philosophers – including himself!

Until the 1950s, many astronomers believed they were extinct volcanoes. After spaceprobes and the Apollo astronauts visited the Moon, scientists realised the craters were blasted out by asteroids and comets that brutally bombarded the Moon in its infancy.

Damian Peach took a two-pane mosaic of Comet Lovejoy C/2012 Q2 by remote observing with a Takahashi 150mm refractor in Nerpio, Spain. Each pane consists of a mono 20-minute exposure (to capture the faint tail) and 2-minute exposures through each of red, green and blue filters for the colour. He had to apply considerable image processing to separate out the moving comet and tails from the stationary starry background.

The Earth suffered, too, but weather and geological activity have smoothed over its cosmic scars. Not so the Moon. With virtually no atmosphere, its impact history is there for all to see. The most ferocious assault took place 3.8 billion years ago, during the Late Heavy Bombardment. This gouged out enormous craters, up to 1200 kilometres across, later filled by dark lava to make up the face of the 'Man in the Moon'.

Best time to see craters? When the Moon is half-lit, and the Sun's illumination comes side-on.

SEPTEMBER'S PICTURE

Terry Lovejoy in Queensland has discovered *six* comets – and, by tradition, they're all named after him. This one hove into his view in August 2014.

Comets are 'dirty snowballs': small lumps of ice and rock that originate in a huge swarm of debris (the Oort Cloud) surrounding the Solar System (see June's Topic).

Comet Lovejoy was very active. Its evaporating ice included 21 organic molecules, including enough alcohol to fill 500 bottles of wine every second! This bolstered the idea that comets seeded Earth with molecules capable of forming life.

Despite its brilliance, the icy nucleus of Lovejoy is quite small, though there's an argument among astronomers who reckon it's only 0.1 kilometres across and those who go for 10 kilometres.

OBSERVING TIP

When you first go out to observe, you may be disappointed at how few stars you can see in the sky. But wait for 20 minutes, and you'll be amazed at how your night vision improves. One reason for this 'dark adaption' is that the pupil of your eye grows larger. More importantly, in dark conditions the retina of your eye builds up bigger reserves of rhodopsin, the chemical that responds to light.

SUNDAY	MONDAY	TUESDAY	WEDNESDAY	THURSDAY	FRIDAY	SATURDAY
30 Moon occults Hyades (am)						1 Venus very close to Spica
2	3 3.37 am Last Quarter Moon; Moon very close to Aldebaran (am)	4	5	6 Mercury very close to Regulus (am; Chart 9b)	7 Neptune at opposition	8
9 7.01 pm New Moon	10 Comet Giacobini-Zinner perihelion, and closest to Earth	11	12 Moon near Venus	13 Moon near Jupiter	14	15 Moon near Antares
16	17 0.15 am First Quarter Moon; Moon near Saturn	18	19 Moon near Mars	20	21	22
23 Autumn Equinox	24	25 3.53 am Full Moon	26	27	28	29 Moon occults Hyades

SPECIAL EVENTS

- **Night of 2/3 September:** the Moon rises in the middle of the Hyades star cluster. You'll see it skim just above Aldebaran around 1.30 am.
- **7 September:** Neptune is opposite to the Sun in the sky and at its closest to Earth this year, 4328 million km away (see Planet Watch).
- **10 September:** Comet Giacobini-Zinner is closest to the Sun (just outside Earth's orbit), and only 58 million km from Earth. It should be a binocular object at magnitude +7, and there'll be some lovely views of it passing the star clusters M37, M35 and NGC 2264 (Chart 9a). It just may erupt to naked-eye brightness.
- **23 September:** the Autumn Equinox occurs at 2.54 am.
- **Night of 29/30 September:** just before midnight, the Moon starts to move in front of outlying stars in the Hyades cluster. By dawn, it's clearing the cluster and moving in on Aldebaran.
- This month, NASA plans to launch its powerful new rocket, the Space Launch System, which will send tiny CubeSats to the Moon.

9a 2/3–24/25 September. Comet Giacobini-Zinner (tail exaggerated).

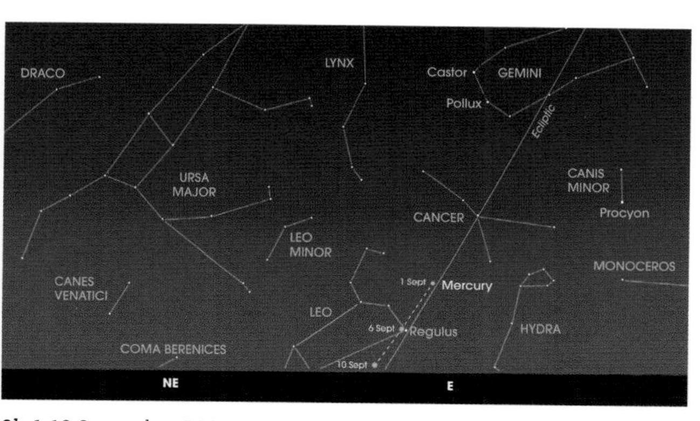

9b 1–10 September, 5.30 am. Mercury conjunction with Regulus.

- At the beginning of the month, you can still catch **Venus** valiantly shining in the dusk twilight, at magnitude –4.5 low down in the west. After six months as the Evening Star, it finally sinks below the horizon by the end of September.
- The bright object to the upper left of Venus is giant planet **Jupiter** (magnitude –1.9) in Libra, and setting about 9 pm.
- **Saturn** lies low in the south, in Sagittarius. The ringworld shines at magnitude +0.4, and sets around 11.30 pm.
- It's followed by **Mars**, setting about 1.30 am. The Red Planet is a fading jewel adorning the celestial Sea Goat, Capricornus, its brightness dropping from –2.1 to –1.3 during September.
- **Neptune** lies above the horizon all night long in Aquarius, reaching opposition on **7 September** (see Special Events). The most distant planet is at its brightest this month, but at magnitude +7.8 you'll need binoculars – or, better, a small telescope – to see it at all.
- Rising around 8.30 pm, fellow water-world **Uranus** lies in Aries and shines at magnitude +5.7.
- If you're up before dawn at the start of September, look out for tiny **Mercury** putting on a brave showing as the sky begins to brighten (Chart 9b). You'll find the innermost planet very low in the east-north-east about 5 am, at magnitude --0.8. It passes Regulus (at one-tenth Mercury's brightness) on **6 September**, and brightens to –1.3 before it disappears into the twilight glow about **10 September**.

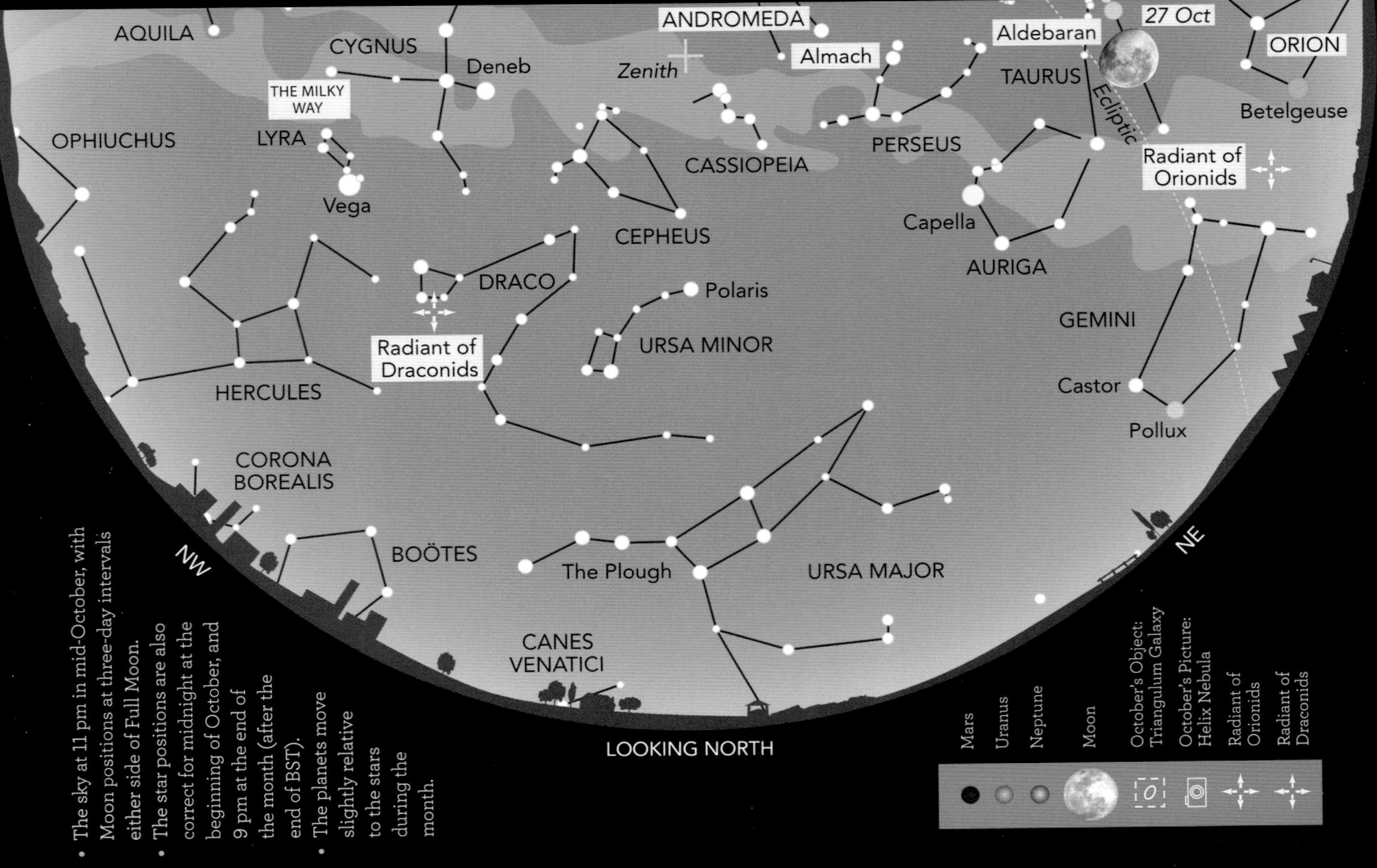

- The sky at 11 pm in mid-October, with Moon positions at three-day intervals either side of Full Moon.
- The star positions are also correct for midnight at the beginning of October, and 9 pm at the end of the month (after the end of BST).
- The planets move slightly relative to the stars during the month.

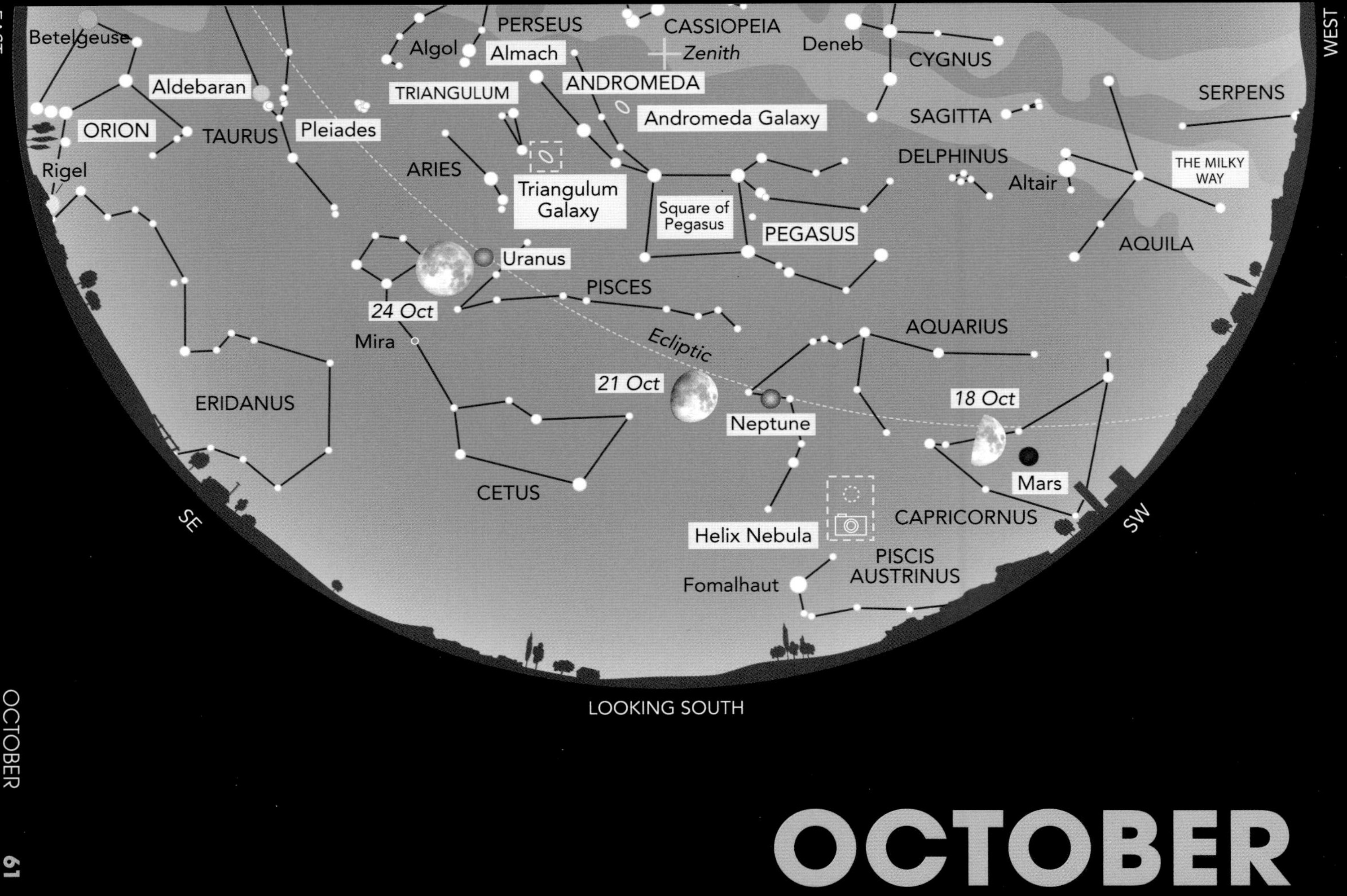
EAST
WEST
Betelgeuse
Aldebaran
ORION
TAURUS
Pleiades
Rigel
Algol
Almach
PERSEUS
CASSIOPEIA
Zenith
Deneb
CYGNUS
TRIANGULUM
ANDROMEDA
Andromeda Galaxy
SAGITTA
SERPENS
ARIES
Triangulum Galaxy
Square of Pegasus
DELPHINUS
Altair
THE MILKY WAY
PEGASUS
AQUILA
Uranus
PISCES
24 Oct
Mira
AQUARIUS
Ecliptic
21 Oct
18 Oct
Neptune
ERIDANUS
Mars
CETUS
Helix Nebula
CAPRICORNUS
SE
SW
PISCIS AUSTRINUS
Fomalhaut
LOOKING SOUTH
OCTOBER

The glories of October's skies can best be described as 'subtle'. The barren **Square of Pegasus** dominates the southern sky, with **Andromeda** attached to his side. But the dull autumn constellations are already being faced down by the brilliant lights of winter, spearheaded by the beautiful star cluster of the **Pleiades**. From Greece to Australia, these stars were seen as a gaggle of girls pursued by an aggressive male – **Aldebaran** or **Orion**.

OCTOBER'S CONSTELLATION

It takes considerable imagination to see the simple line of stars making up **Andromeda** as a young princess chained to a rock, about to be gobbled up by a sea monster – but that's ancient legends for you (see September's Constellation). Andromeda contains some surprising delights. **Almach**, the star at the left-hand end of the line, is a lovely sight through small telescopes: this beautiful double star comprises a yellow supergiant shining 2000 times brighter than the Sun, and a fainter bluish companion, which is in fact triple.

OBSERVING TIP

Don't think that you need a telescope to bring the heavens closer. Binoculars are excellent – and you can fling them into the back of the car at the last minute. For astronomy, buy binoculars with large lenses coupled with a modest magnification. An ideal size for astronomy are 7 × 50 binoculars, meaning that the magnification is seven times, and that the diameter of the lenses is 50 millimetres. They have good light grasp, and the low magnification means that they don't exaggerate the wobbles of your arms too much. Even so, it's best to rest your binoculars on a wall or a fence to steady the image. (See pages 86–9 for more about binoculars.)

But the glory of Andromeda is its great galaxy, beautifully placed on October nights. Lying above the line of stars, the **Andromeda Galaxy** is the most distant object easily visible to the unaided eye, a mind-boggling 2.5 million light years away. The Andromeda Galaxy is the biggest member of the Local Group of galaxies, containing 400 billion stars. It is a wonderful sight with binoculars or a small telescope.

OCTOBER'S OBJECT

This month, we have a little known extragalactic neighbour, the **Triangulum Galaxy**. To find the elusive beast, start with the great Andromeda Galaxy and then – preferably with binoculars or a low-powered telescope – move the same distance below the line of stars making up the constellation of Andromeda. In the faint but distinctive star pattern of **Triangulum** (the Triangle), you should hit another fuzzy patch of light. Under exceptional conditions, the Triangulum Galaxy is *just* visible to the unaided eye (although it helps to be in a desert!).

But it's a challenge to see any detail in this scruffy little spiral even through a moderate telescope. It has a very low surface brightness, and – at three million light years distance – it's slightly further away than the Andromeda Galaxy.

The Helix Nebula photographed through a 685 mm Corrected Dall-Kirkham reflector at Siding Spring Observatory in Australia. Damian Peach remotely controlled the telescope from his Sussex home to take a total of 2 hours of exposures with a mono FLI ProLine PL09000 camera plus red, green and blue filters.

The Triangulum Galaxy (catalogued as M33) is the third largest galaxy in the Local Group, and is home to 40 billion stars: one-tenth the population of our **Milky Way**. But it's a hotbed of star formation, boasting an enormous star factory, **NGC 604**, which measures 1500 light years across.

OCTOBER'S TOPIC: GALAXIES

With the Andromeda Galaxy and Triangulum Galaxy riding high, and the stars of our own Milky Way Galaxy all around us, it's time to take a look at the star cities that populate the Universe. These three are all *spiral galaxies* – they're rich in gas and dust poised to make new generations of stars, and adorned with beautiful curving arms made of young, hot stars. *Irregular galaxies* have a similar mix of ingredients, but are too small to 'grow' arms. If you visit the southern hemisphere, you can see our two irregular companions, the Large and Small Magellanic Clouds, shining brightly in the sky. *Elliptical galaxies* are the third type. They range from the very small to the truly gargantuan, some with trillions of stars. But most of their stars are old and red; there's very little by way of building materials in these galaxies to make new stars. A few galaxies are violent, with brilliant jets of gas shooting out from the vicinity of a central black hole at speeds close to the velocity of light.

OCTOBER'S PICTURE

Will this be the end for our Sun? The **Helix Nebula** in Aquarius was once a normal star, but in its death throes it jettisoned its outer atmosphere – fluorescing in a greenish glow as it's heated by radiation from the core of the old star, now cooling to become a white dwarf.

The Helix is 2.5 light years across. At 700 light years, it's the closest of the planetary nebulae – so-called because they look a bit like distant planets. The parent star shed its atmosphere 10,000 years ago. The same fate will befall the Sun. But don't panic: there are still seven billion years to go!

SUNDAY	MONDAY	TUESDAY	WEDNESDAY	THURSDAY	FRIDAY	SATURDAY
	1	2 10.45 am Last Quarter Moon	3	4	5	6 Moon near Regulus (am)
7	8 Draconid meteor shower	9 Draconid meteor shower (am); 4.47 am New Moon	10	11 Moon near Jupiter (Chart 10b)	12	13
14 Moon near Saturn (Chart 10b)	15	16 7.02 pm First Quarter Moon	17	18 Moon near Mars (Chart 10b)	19	20
21 Orionid meteor shower	22 Orionid meteor shower (am)	23	24 5.45 pm Full Moon; Uranus at opposition	25	26	27 Moon near Aldebaran (am)
28 2 am BST ends	29	30	31 4.40 pm Last Quarter Moon			

SPECIAL EVENTS

- **Night of 8/9 October:** maximum of the **Draconid** meteor shower. Normally a measly display, we may be in for a treat as Giacobini-Zinner – the comet shedding the meteor particles – passed unusually close to the Earth last month.
- **Night of 21/22 October:** maximum of the **Orionid** meteor shower, but bright moonlight interferes this year.
- **24 October:** Uranus is opposite to the Sun in the sky and at its closest to Earth this year, 2824 million km away (see Planet Watch).
- **28 October, 2 am:** end of British Summer Time.
- For the first half of the month, Comet Giacobini-Zinner is a binocular object in the morning sky, around magnitude +8. It passes the star cluster M50 in the early hours of 8 October. (Chart 10a).
- Launches this month: the European Space Agency's Solar Orbiter to study the Sun in close-up; BepiColombo to orbit and study Mercury; the international James Webb Space Telescope to investigate the early Universe and planets of other stars.

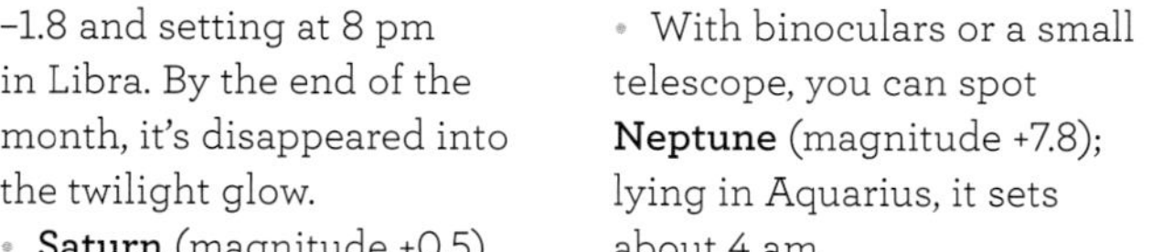

10a 2/3–12/13 October. Comet Giacobini-Zinner (tail exaggerated).

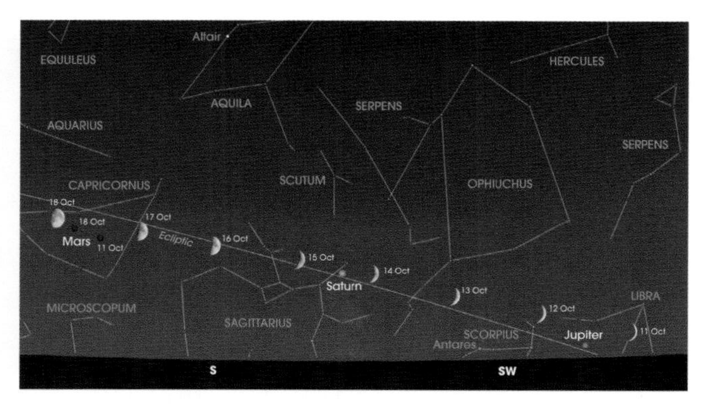

10b 11–18 October, 7 pm. Moon with Jupiter, Saturn and Mars.

- At the start of October, you may catch **Jupiter** very low in the south-west, at magnitude –1.8 and setting at 8 pm in Libra. By the end of the month, it's disappeared into the twilight glow.
- **Saturn** (magnitude +0.5) lies in Sagittarius and sets around 9.30 pm.
- To its left, **Mars** is the brightest planet in the late evening sky. Moving through Capricornus and setting about 0.30 am, the Red Planet fades from magnitude –1.3 to –0.6 during October.
- With binoculars or a small telescope, you can spot **Neptune** (magnitude +7.8); lying in Aquarius, it sets about 4 am.
- **Uranus** is at its closest to Earth (see Special Events); at magnitude +5.7 the planet is just visible to the naked eye, but much more easily seen with binoculars. Visible all night long, you'll find the seventh planet on the border of Aries and Pisces.

Uranus

- **Mercury** and **Venus** are too close to the Sun to be visible this month.

- The sky at 10 pm in mid-November, with Moon positions at three-day intervals either side of Full Moon.
- The star positions are also correct for 11 pm at the beginning of November, and 9 pm at the end of the month.
- The planets move slightly relative to the stars during the month.

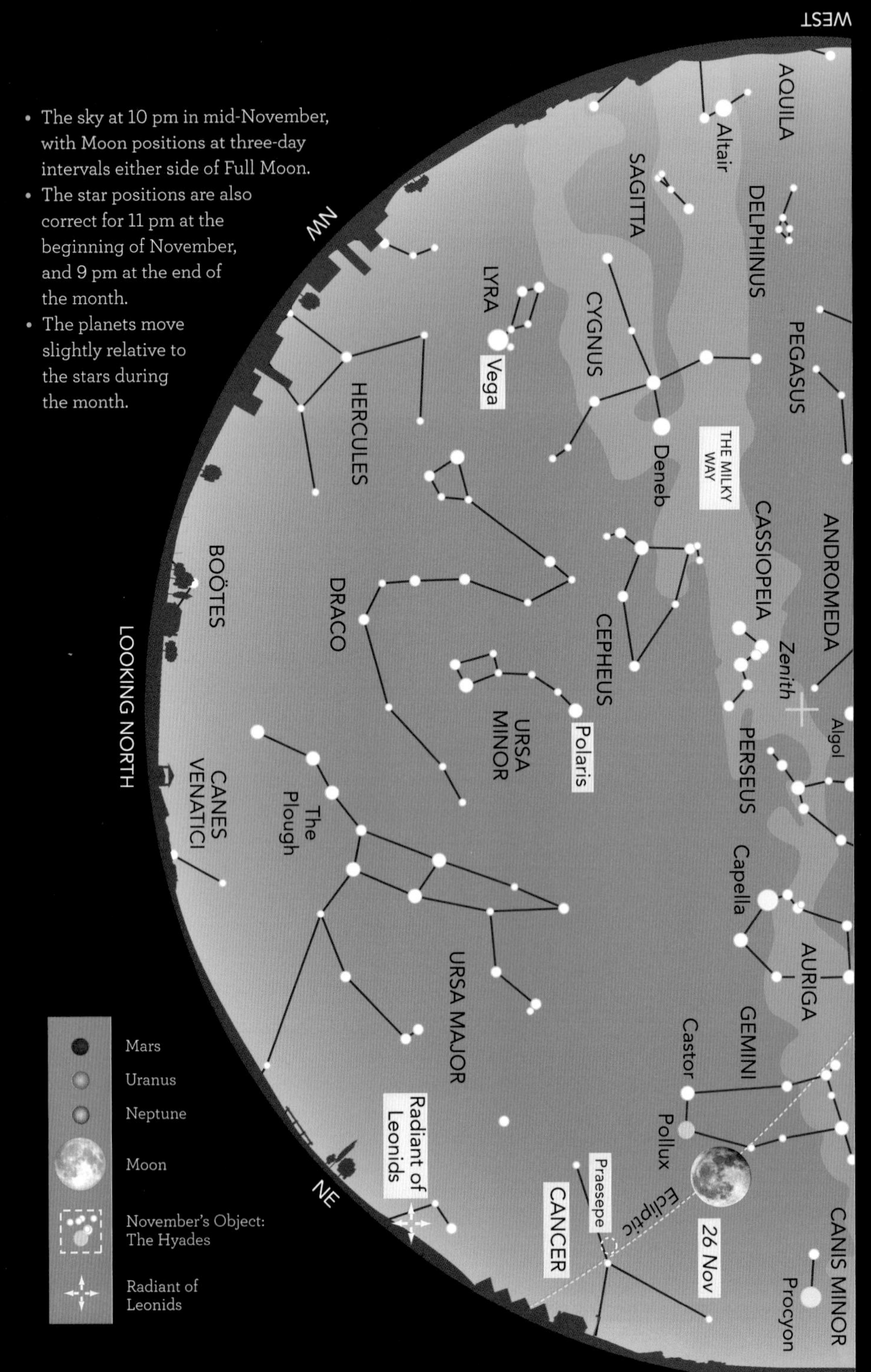

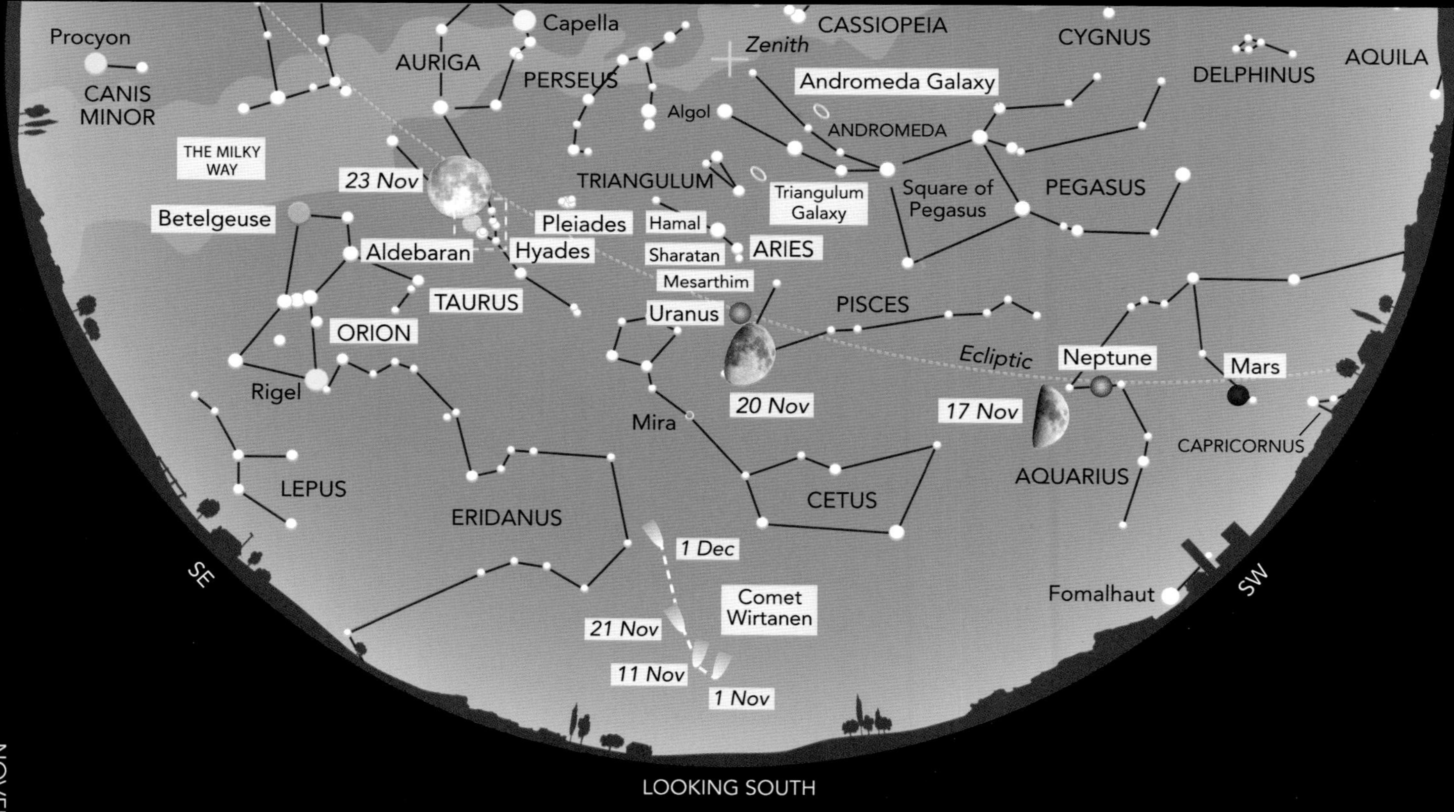
EAST
Procyon
CANIS MINOR
AURIGA
Capella
PERSEUS
CASSIOPEIA
Zenith
CYGNUS
DELPHINUS
AQUILA
WEST
Andromeda Galaxy
Algol
ANDROMEDA
THE MILKY WAY
23 Nov
TRIANGULUM
Triangulum Galaxy
Square of Pegasus
PEGASUS
Betelgeuse
Pleiades
Hamal
Aldebaran
Hyades
Sharatan
ARIES
Mesarthim
TAURUS
PISCES
Uranus
ORION
Ecliptic
Neptune
Mars
Rigel
20 Nov
17 Nov
Mira
CAPRICORNUS
LEPUS
AQUARIUS
CETUS
ERIDANUS
1 Dec
SE
Comet Wirtanen
Fomalhaut
SW
21 Nov
11 Nov
1 Nov
LOOKING SOUTH

NOVEMBER

The **Milky Way** rears overhead on these dark November nights, providing a stunning inside perspective on the huge Galaxy that is our home in space. Look carefully, and you can see that it's spangled with fuzzy glowing diadems. Even better, sweep the band of the Milky Way with binoculars or a small telescope, and these blurry jewels appear in their true guise: distant clusters of stars.

NOVEMBER'S CONSTELLATION

Aries is not a constellation that instantly grabs you. It has two moderately bright stars (**Hamal** and **Sheratan**), which – with fainter **Mesarthim** – make up the head of the celestial ram.

However, it's a very ancient constellation. Around 2000 years ago, the Sun crossed the celestial equator in Aries, a celebration that spring was on the way, as the Sun climbed higher in northern skies. In Greek mythology, the ram had an unfortunate ending. The 'Golden Ram' that rescued the hero Phrixos was eventually sacrificed to the gods, and his skin hung in the temple as the coveted 'golden fleece'.

Of the three main stars, Mesarthim – the faintest – is the most interesting. It's a double star, consisting of two equally bright white stars easily visible through a small telescope.

NOVEMBER'S OBJECT

According to legend, the 'V'-shaped **Hyades** star cluster, forming the 'head' of **Taurus** (the Bull), was a group of nymphs who cared for Bacchus as a baby – though we prefer the Roman interpretation as 'little pigs' or the Chinese vision of a 'rabbit net'.

The Hyades is the nearest star cluster to the Earth, lying 153 light years away. It contains about 200 stars, some 625 million years old – very young on the stellar scale. The Hyades may have a celestial twin, too: **Praesepe** – the Beehive Cluster in **Cancer** – is the same age, and moving in the same direction.

Although **Aldebaran**, marking the bull's angry eye, looks as though it's in the Hyades, this red giant just happens to lie in the same direction, and at less than half the distance.

NOVEMBER'S TOPIC: SUPERNOVAE

Brilliant red **Betelgeuse** in **Orion** is a familiar landmark in November's skies. But it won't be there forever. One day within the next million years Betelgeuse will die – in a violent supernova explosion that will have dire consequences for life on any planets nearby.

A star more than eight times heavier than the Sun is doomed to an early death, as it rips through the nuclear fuel that powers its energy. Our modest Sun converts hydrogen to helium, but the biggies become far more ambitious. When the hydrogen has run out, gravity squeezes tighter, building successively heavier elements in the star's central nuclear reactor.

All goes well until the core is made of iron. Trying to fuse iron is a fatal mistake, as this reaction takes *in* energy. The star's core catastrophically collapses. A burst

OBSERVING TIP

The **Andromeda Galaxy** is often described as the furthest object 'easily visible to the unaided eye'. But it can be a bit elusive – especially if you are suffering from light pollution (see page 90 for more about light pollution). The trick is to memorise Andromeda's pattern of stars, and then to look slightly to the *side* of where you expect the galaxy to be. This technique – called 'averted vision' – causes the image to fall on the outer region of your retina, which is more sensitive to light than the central region that's evolved to discern fine details. You'll certainly need averted vision to track down Andromeda's fainter sibling, the **Triangulum Galaxy**, with the naked eye. The technique is also crucial when you want to observe the faintest nebulae or galaxies through a telescope.

of neutrinos blasts through its outer layers, blowing the star apart. At maximum brightness, a supernova can outshine a whole galaxy of 100 billion stars.

The supernova hurls a cornucopia of elements into space, those from inside the dead star, and others created in the inferno of the explosion. And – in the end – a supernova is a phoenix: for out of its ashes, the seeds of life will arise.

NOVEMBER'S PICTURE

Because Earth's spin axis points almost directly at the Pole Star, we seem to rotate 'underneath' it. In this long exposure image, the stars around the celestial pole trace out long arcs, showing off beautifully the colours and brightnesses of the circumpolar stars. The alignment with **Polaris** isn't exact, so the Pole Star shows up as a small comma here. Pole stars don't last forever, changing as the Earth's axis 'wobbles' in space: around AD 14,000, brilliant **Vega** will lie close to the Pole.

Mary Spicer took 156 consecutive exposures over a period of 63 minutes, using a fixed Canon 1100D camera with an 18 mm f/3.6 lens. Each was 30 seconds long, at ISO1600. Because cloud rolled over some of them, she stacked 127 images using StarStax, tweaked slightly in Lightroom. The tree was light-painted, courtesy of a neighbour's security light!

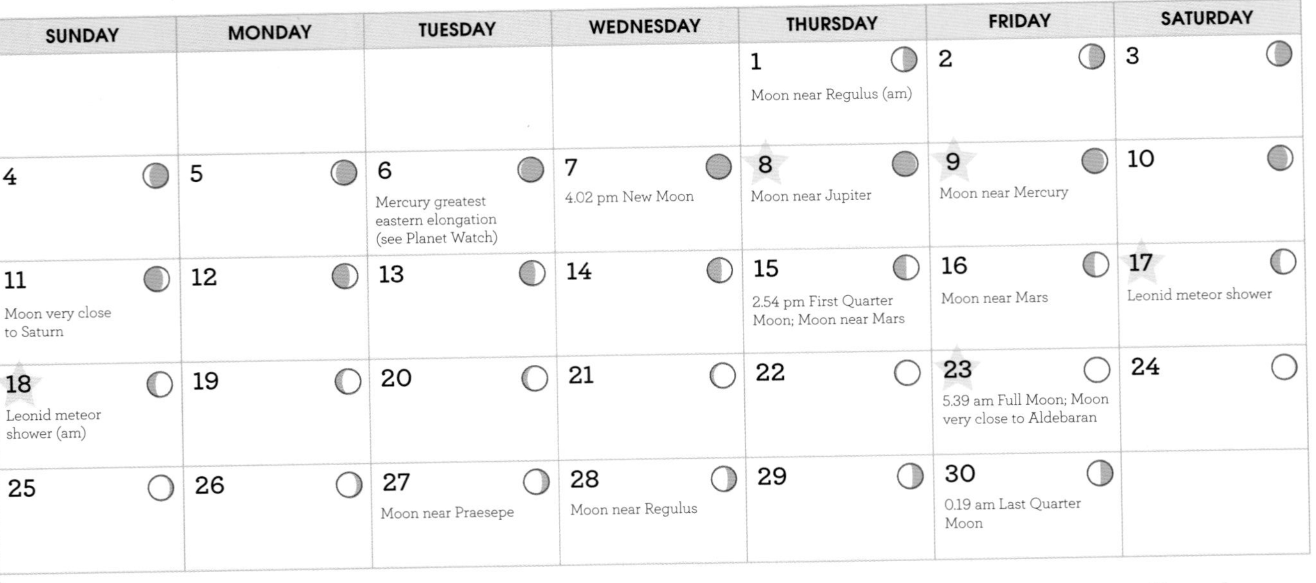

SUNDAY	MONDAY	TUESDAY	WEDNESDAY	THURSDAY	FRIDAY	SATURDAY
				1 Moon near Regulus (am)	2	3
4	5	6 Mercury greatest eastern elongation (see Planet Watch)	7 4.02 pm New Moon	8 Moon near Jupiter	9 Moon near Mercury	10
11 Moon very close to Saturn	12	13	14	15 2.54 pm First Quarter Moon; Moon near Mars	16 Moon near Mars	17 Leonid meteor shower
18 Leonid meteor shower (am)	19	20	21	22	23 5.39 am Full Moon; Moon very close to Aldebaran	24
25	26	27 Moon near Praesepe	28 Moon near Regulus	29	30 0.19 am Last Quarter Moon	

SPECIAL EVENTS

- **8 and 9 November:** use binoculars to check out the very thin crescent Moon with Jupiter, Mercury and Saturn, low in the south-west after sunset (Chart 11a).
- **Night of 17/18 November:** maximum of the **Leonid** meteor shower, enhanced this year as the Earth is crossing a dense stream of debris from Comet Tempel-Tuttle. Best to observe after 1 am, when the Moon has set.
- **23 November:** as it grows dark, you'll find the Full Moon in the midst of the Hyades star cluster; around 8 pm it skims past Aldebaran.
- **Comet Wirtanen** appears in the evening sky this month, on its way to a great show in December. Discovered by Carl Wirtanen in 1948, this celestial visitor orbits the Sun in just four and a half years. It starts November as a binocular object (magnitude +7.3) low on the southern horizon, and brightens as it ascends through Cetus to become visible to the naked eye – at magnitude +4.8 – by the end of the month (see the Star Chart).

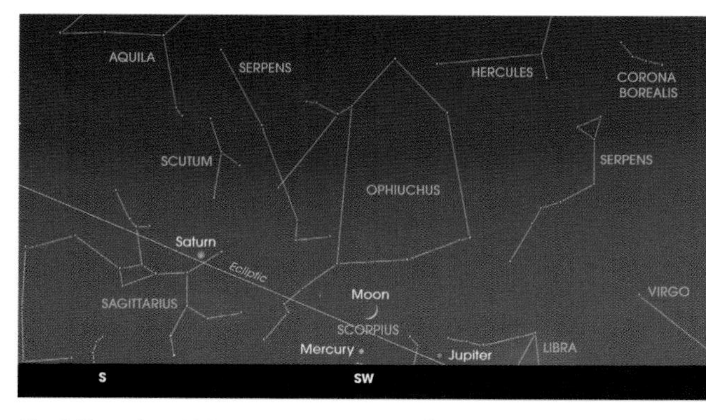

11a *9 November, 4.30 pm. Crescent Moon with Jupiter, Mercury and Saturn.*

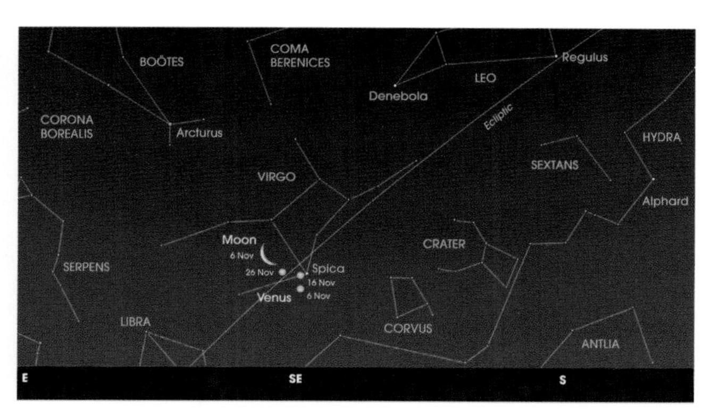

11b *6–26 November, 7 am. Venus, Spica and crescent Moon.*

• Though **Mercury** is at its greatest elongation from the Sun on **6 November**, it's hardly visible against the

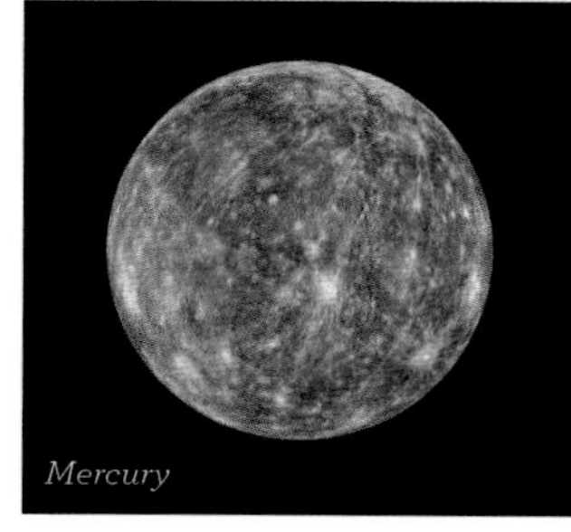

twilight glow as seen from Britain. Your best chance of catching it is on **9 November**, when the innermost planet – at magnitude –0.1 – lies below the crescent Moon (see Special Events and Chart 11a).

• Though it's brighter at magnitude –1.7, giant **Jupiter** is also overwhelmed by the brightness of the dusk twilight. It appears very low in the south-west in Libra just after sunset.

• **Saturn** lies higher in the south-west, shining at magnitude +0.6 in Sagittarius and setting around 6.30 pm.

• The later evening sky is dominated by **Mars**, which is setting about 11.30 pm. Mars fades from magnitude –0.6 to 0.0 as it travels from Capricornus to Aquarius.

• **Neptune** is lurking in Aquarius, at a dim magnitude +7.9: the most distant planet sets around 1 am. You'll find **Uranus** (magnitude +5.7) on the border of Aries and Pisces, setting about 5 am.

• There's a treat in store for early birds, as **Venus** roars into view as the Morning Star. At the start of November, it's rising in the dawn twilight at magnitude –4.1; by the end of the month, it has brightened to magnitude –4.4 and rises almost 4 hours before the Sun. The star near Venus mid-month is Spica (Chart 11b).

NOVEMBER'S PLANET WATCH

- The sky at 10 pm in mid-December, with Moon positions at three-day intervals either side of Full Moon.
- The star positions are also correct for 11 pm at the beginning of December, and 9 pm at the end of the month.
- The planets move slightly relative to the stars during the month.

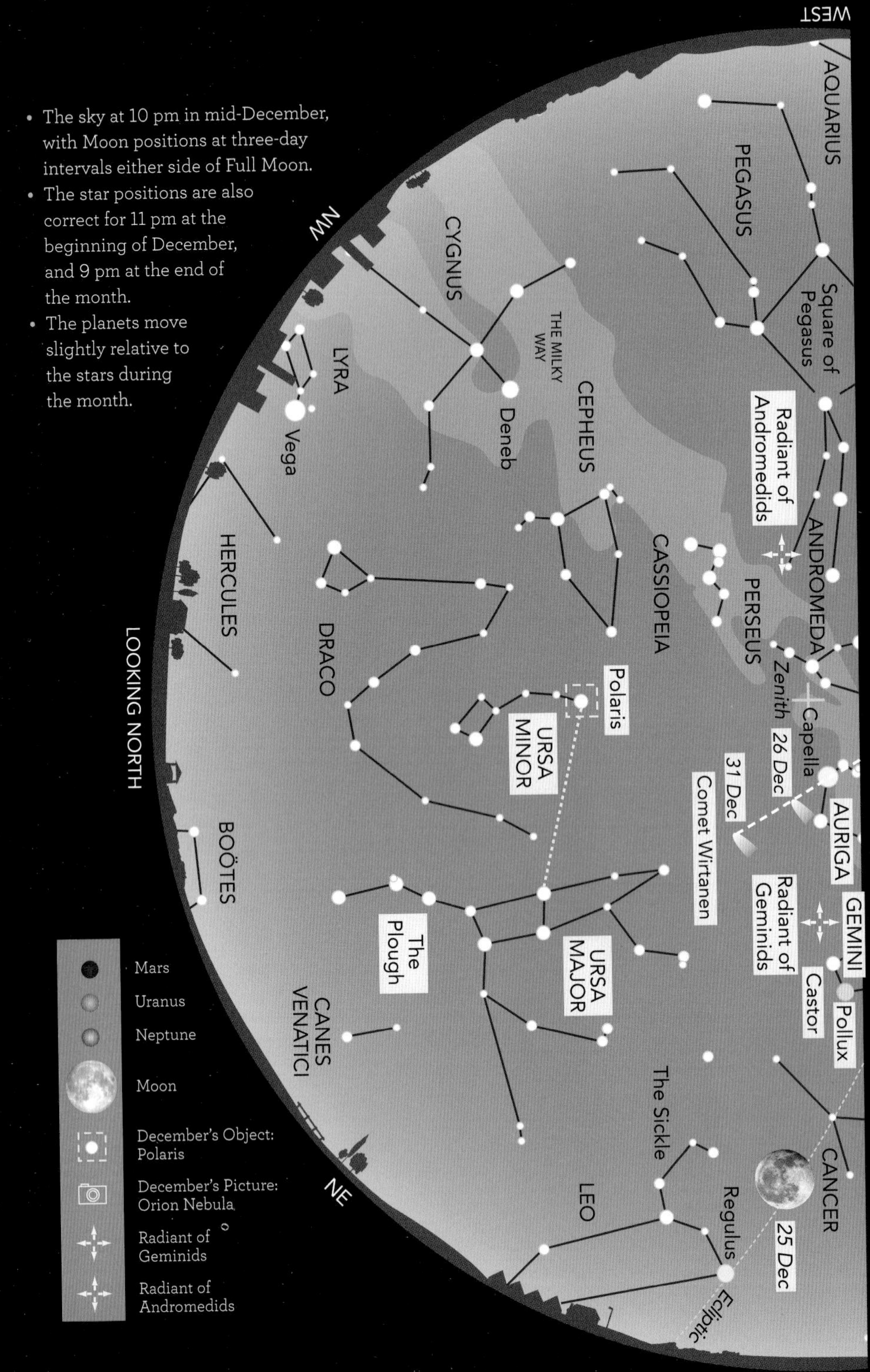

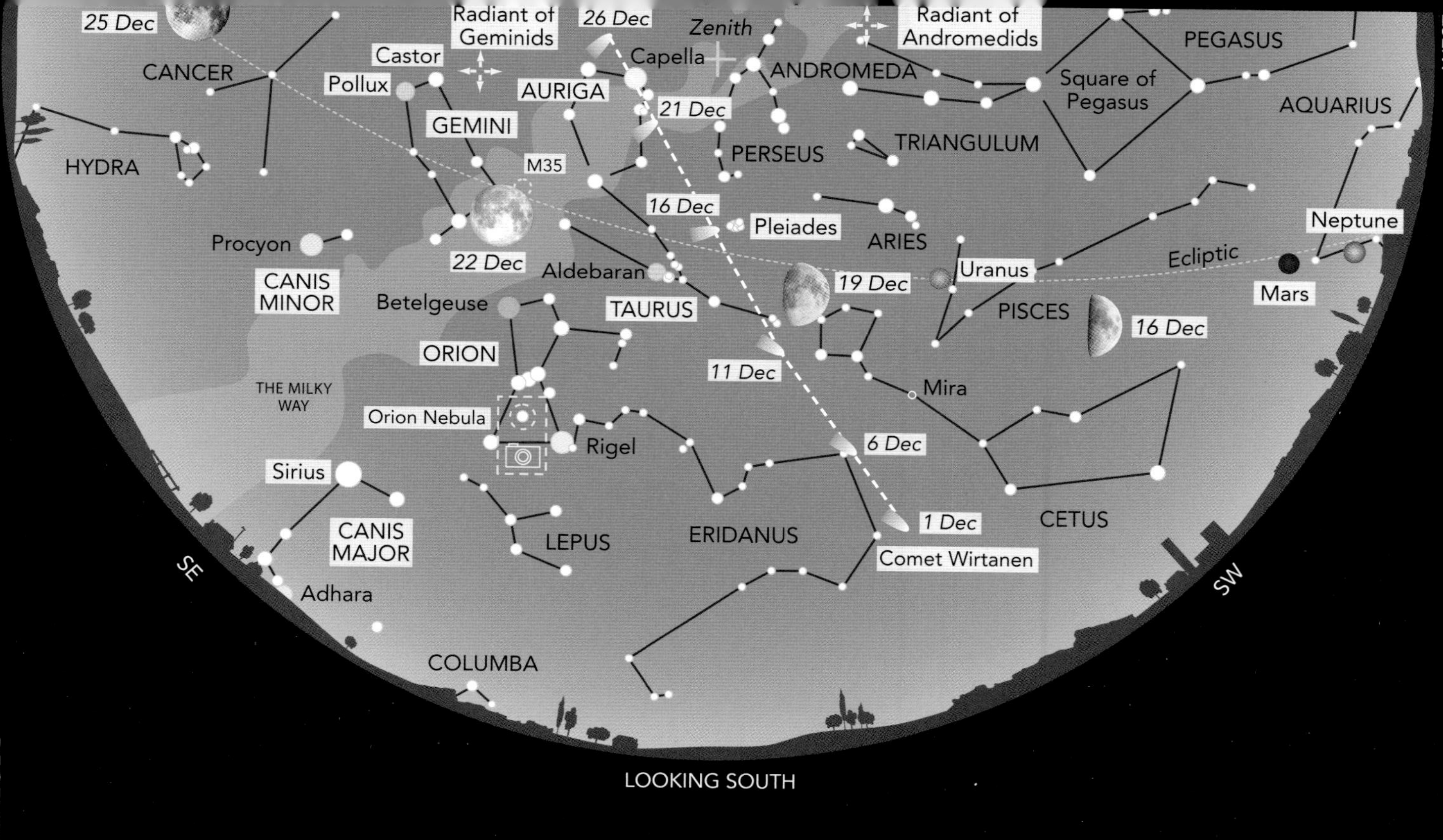
EAST
WEST
25 Dec
Radiant of Geminids
26 Dec
Zenith
Radiant of Andromedids
PEGASUS
Castor
Capella
CANCER
Pollux
AURIGA
ANDROMEDA
Square of Pegasus
AQUARIUS
21 Dec
GEMINI
TRIANGULUM
PERSEUS
HYDRA
M35
16 Dec
Pleiades
Neptune
ARIES
Procyon
Ecliptic
22 Dec
Aldebaran
Uranus
19 Dec
Mars
CANIS MINOR
Betelgeuse
TAURUS
PISCES
16 Dec
ORION
11 Dec
Mira
THE MILKY WAY
Orion Nebula
6 Dec
Rigel
Sirius
1 Dec
CETUS
CANIS MAJOR
LEPUS
ERIDANUS
Comet Wirtanen
SE
SW
Adhara
COLUMBA
LOOKING SOUTH

DECEMBER

We have a Christmas comet! This month, all eyes will be on **Comet Wirtanen**, as it slowly glides through the night sky – an unforgettable sight on 16 December when the comet passes the **Pleiades** star cluster, the Seven Sisters. We're also treated to the best shooting-star display of the year, and some stunning planets in the morning sky. Not to forget the regular brilliant constellations of winter: **Orion**, his hunting dogs **Canis Major** and **Canis Minor**, **Taurus** (the Bull), the hero twins of **Gemini**, and the charioteer **Auriga** almost overhead.

DECEMBER'S CONSTELLATION

Well known as the Twins, **Gemini** is crowned by the bright stars **Castor** and **Pollux** representing the heads of the celestial brethren, with their bodies running in parallel lines of stars. In legend they were conceived by princess Leda on her wedding night – Castor by her husband, and immortal Pollux by Zeus, who invaded the marital suite disguised as a swan. The devoted pair were placed together for eternity among the stars.

Castor is an amazing family of six stars. Through a small telescope, you can see that Castor is double. Spectroscopes reveal that both these stars are themselves double. Then there's an outlying star, visible through a telescope, which also turns out to be double.

Pollux – slightly brighter than Castor – boasts a huge planet: a mighty world bigger than Jupiter.

The constellation contains a pretty star cluster, **M35**. Even at a distance of 2800 light years, it's visible to the unaided eye, and a fine sight through binoculars or a small telescope.

DECEMBER'S OBJECT

The Pole Star – **Polaris** – is a surprisingly shy animal, coming in at the modest magnitude of +2.0. Find it by following the two end stars of the **Plough** (see the Star Chart) in **Ursa Major** (the Great Bear). Polaris lies at the end of the tail of the Little Bear (**Ursa Minor**), and it pulsates in size, making its brightness vary slightly over a period of four days. But its importance centres on the fact that Earth's North Pole points towards Polaris, so we spin 'underneath' it. It remains almost stationary in the sky, and acts as a fixed point for both astronomy and navigation. Over a 26,000-year period, the Earth's axis swings around like an

OBSERVING TIP

With Christmas on the way, you may well be thinking of buying a telescope as a present for a budding stargazer. Beware! Unscrupulous websites and mail-order catalogues often advertise small telescopes that boast huge magnifications. This is 'empty magnification' – blowing up an image that the lens or mirror simply doesn't have the ability to get to grips with, so all you see is a bigger blur. The maximum magnification a telescope can actually provide is twice the diameter of the lens or mirror in millimetres. So if you see an advertisement for a 75 mm telescope, beware of any claims for a magnification greater than 150 times. (See pages 86–9 for more about telescopes.)

The Orion Nebula, M42, photographed by Andrew Davies from Astrofarm in France using an Altair 80 mm refractor on an iOptron CEM60 mount and an Altair Hypercam IMX178 colour CCD camera. He took a total of 56 minutes' exposure time, with individual frames ranging from 1 minute to 5 minutes to capture the different brightness levels of the nebula.

old-fashioned spinning top – a phenomenon called precession – so our 'pole stars' change with time.

DECEMBER'S TOPIC: WHITE DWARFS

Brilliant **Sirius** is accompanied by a most extraordinary companion star, which was first predicted by its gravitational pull on the Dog Star: the small companion is often fondly nicknamed 'the Pup'. At magnitude +8.5, the Pup should be visible through binoculars. But Sirius glares at magnitude –1.47, and the contrast makes the Pup a devil to find: you'll need a telescope with a mirror at least 300 mm across.

The Pup is only the size of the Earth, yet it boasts 98 per cent of the mass of our Sun. Such 'white dwarfs' make up 10 per cent of all the stars in the Galaxy. A white dwarf is the core of an old star that has died, having puffed off its atmosphere as a brief – but glorious – planetary nebula. The core has collapsed under its own gravity, squeezing electrons and the nuclei of atoms together to unbelievable densities: a *matchboxful* of white-dwarf material would outweigh an elephant!

With no power source, a white dwarf eventually just fades away, to end up as a cold, black cinder. Seven billion years hence, this is the fate that awaits our Sun.

DECEMBER'S PICTURE

Part of the huge Orion star-forming complex, the **Orion Nebula** is visible to the unaided eye, just below the Hunter's belt – and it's a beautiful sight through binoculars or a small telescope. Some 24 light years across, and 1300 light years away, the Orion Nebula is a hotbed of activity, as highlighted in Andrew's image. The nebula weighs in at 2000 Suns; while the surrounding dark clouds could yield 100,000 stars in years to come. Watch out for fireworks!

DECEMBER'S CALENDAR

SUNDAY	MONDAY	TUESDAY	WEDNESDAY	THURSDAY	FRIDAY	SATURDAY
30	31					1
2	3 Moon near Venus (am)	4 Moon near Venus (am)	5	6 Moon near Mercury and Jupiter (am); Andromedid meteor shower?	7 Andromedid meteor shower? (am); 7.20 am New Moon	8 Moon near Saturn; Moon very close to Neptune (see Planet Watch)
9 Moon near Saturn	10	11	12 Comet Wirtanen perihelion	13 Geminid meteor shower	14 Geminid meteor shower (am); Moon near Mars	15 11.49 am First Quarter Moon; Mercury greatest western elongation
16 Comet Wirtanen nearest to Earth, close to Pleiades (Chart 12b)	17	18	19	20 Moon near Hyades	21 Mercury near Jupiter (am; Chart 12a); Moon occults Hyades (am); Winter Solstice	22 Mercury very close to Jupiter (am; Chart 12a); 5.49 pm Full Moon
23 Comet Wirtanen very close to Capella (Chart 12b)	24	25 Moon very close to Praesepe (am)	26 Moon near Regulus	27	28	29 9.34 am Last Quarter Moon

SPECIAL EVENTS

- **Night of 6/7 December:** we may witness a rare meteor shower – the **Andromedids** – when dust shed by Comet Biela in 1649 impacts the Earth.
- **Night of 13/14 December:** maximum of the spectacular **Geminid** meteor shower, when the Earth hits a stream of interplanetary debris from the asteroid Phaethon. Best observed after moonset.
- **Night of 20/21 December:** the Moon moves in front of the Hyades after midnight, and is next to Aldebaran by dawn.
- **21 December, 10.22 pm:** Winter Solstice, with the shortest night and longest day.
- **Comet Wirtanen** is visible to the naked eye throughout December, reaching magnitude +3 as it comes closest to the Sun (just outside Earth's orbit) on **12 December** and whizzes only 12 million km from the Earth on **16 December**: on that night it will be a stunning sight right next to the Pleiades. On **23 December**, the comet skims only 12 arcminutes from Capella: it could look as though the bright star has sprouted a tail (Chart 12b)!

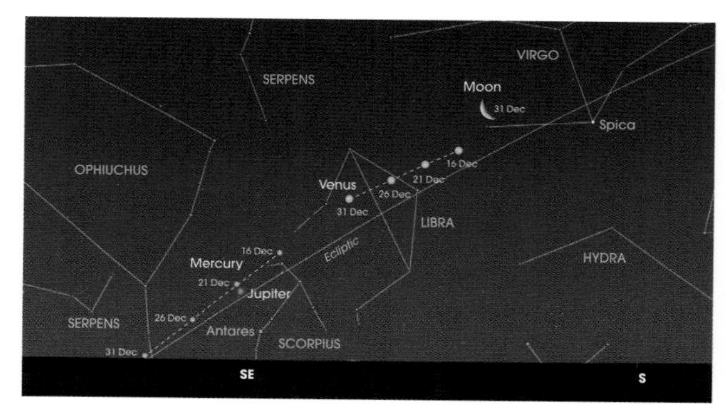

12a *16–31 December, 7 am. Conjunction of Mercury and Jupiter; also Venus and the Moon.*

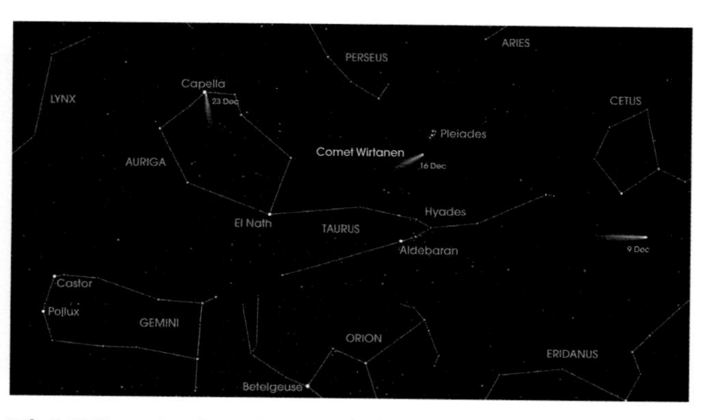

12b *9–23 December. Comet Wirtanen (tail exaggerated).*

- You'll find **Saturn** low in the south-west after sunset. Lying in Sagittarius, the ringworld (magnitude +0.5) sets around 5 pm, and disappears into the twilight glow by the end of December.
- **Mars** lies higher in the evening sky, setting about 11 pm. The planet's distinctive reddish glow fades from magnitude 0.0 to magnitude +0.5 during December, as the planet treks from Aquarius into Pisces.
- On **8 December**, Mars acts as a convenient guide to finding faint **Neptune**. Use binoculars or a small telescope to spot a faint dot 15 arcminutes below the Red Planet, and a thousand times fainter, at magnitude +7.9. It's a conjunction of Solar System's reddest and greenest planets! Neptune, lying in Aquarius, sets around 11 pm.
- **Uranus** (magnitude +5.7) resides on the fringes of Aries and Pisces, setting about 3 am.
- **Venus** is rising around 4 am as the brilliant Morning Star, at magnitude −4.5. It appears dazzlingly bright in the totally dark sky, travelling from near Spica in Virgo through to Libra (Chart 12a).
- To the lower left of Venus, around 7 am, you'll find **Mercury** and **Jupiter** just above the south-east horizon. At the start of December, fainter Mercury (magnitude +0.5) lies above Jupiter, which is second only to Venus at magnitude −1.7. The planets converge, passing less than a degree apart on **21/22 December** in Ophiuchus, when Mercury has doubled in brightness to magnitude −0.4 (Chart 12a).

Can you see the planets? We're amazed when people ask us that question: our nearby cosmic neighbours are the brightest objects in the night sky after the Moon. Being so close, you can watch them getting up to their antics from night to night. Plus, there's planetary debris – the comets and meteors that are leftovers from the birth of the Solar System. All the info you need for observing them is here too.

THE INFERIOR PLANETS

A planet with an orbit that lies closer to the Sun than the orbit of Earth is known as *inferior*. Mercury and Venus are the inferior planets. They show a full range of phases (like the Moon) from the thinnest crescents to full, depending on their position in relation to the Earth and the Sun. The diagram below shows the various positions of the inferior planets. They are invisible when at *conjunction*, when they are either behind the Sun, or between the Earth and the Sun, and lost in the latter's glare.

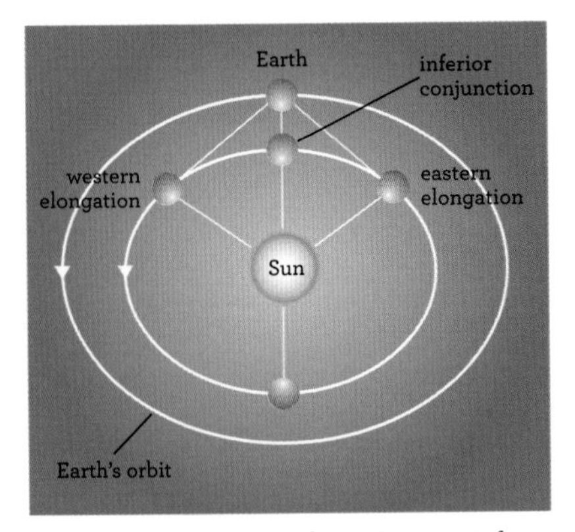

At eastern or western elongation, an inferior planet is at its maximum angular distance from the Sun. Conjunction occurs at two stages in the planet's orbit. Under certain circumstances, an inferior planet can transit across the Sun's disc at inferior conjunction.

Mercury

In the evening sky, we'll have our best views of this elusive planet in the middle of March; Mercury's evening appearances in June–July and November are low in bright twilight sky. The innermost planet puts on good morning shows in January, August–September and December (though it's lost in the dawn twilight at the April apparition).

Maximum elongations of Mercury in 2018

Date	Separation
1 January	23° west
15 March	18° east
29 April	27° west
12 July	26° east
26 August	18° west
6 November	23° east

Venus

For most of the year – from February to September – we can enjoy Venus as the Evening Star, though it's quite low in the dusk twilight. In October, it swings between Sun and Earth, to emerge as a brilliant Morning Star in November and December.

Maximum elongation of Venus in 2018

Date	Separation
17 August	46° east

THE SUPERIOR PLANETS

The superior planets are those with orbits that lie beyond that of the Earth. They are Mars, Jupiter, Saturn, Uranus and Neptune. The best time to observe a superior planet is when the Earth lies between it and the Sun. At this point in a planet's orbit, it is at *opposition*.

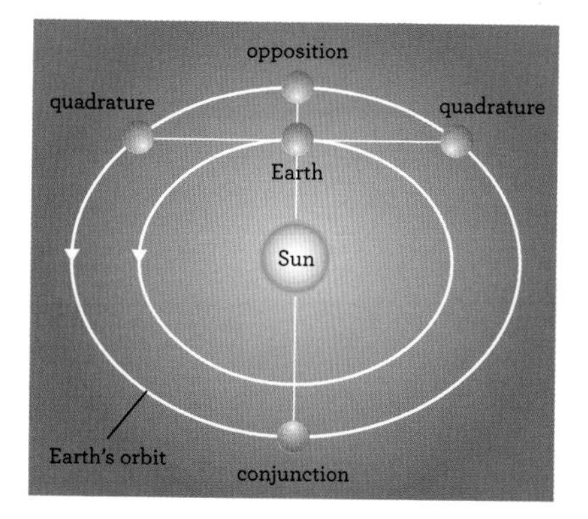

Superior planets are invisible at conjunction. At quadrature the planet is at right angles to the Sun as viewed from Earth. Opposition is the best time to observe a superior planet.

MAGNITUDES

Astronomers measure the brightness of stars, planets and other celestial objects using a scale of magnitudes. Somewhat confusingly, fainter objects have higher magnitudes, while brighter objects have lower magnitudes; the most brilliant stars have negative magnitudes! Naked-eye stars range from magnitude −1.5 for the brightest star, Sirius, to +6.5 for the faintest stars you can see on a really dark night.

As a guide, here are the magnitudes of selected objects:

Sun	−26.7
Full Moon	−12.5
Venus (at its brightest)	−4.7
Sirius	−1.5
Betelgeuse	+0.4
Polaris (Pole Star)	+2.0
Faintest star visible to the naked eye	+6.5
Faintest star visible to the Hubble Space Telescope	+31

Mars

For the first half of the year, you'll need to be up after midnight to catch the Red Planet. It's inexorably brightening towards opposition on **27 July**, when Mars is a stunning sight next to the eclipsed Moon. For the rest of the year, it's gradually fading in the evening sky.

Progress of Mars through the constellations	
January	Libra
Early February	Scorpius
Mid-Feb to mid-March	Ophiuchus
Mid-March to mid-May	Sagittarius
Mid-May to mid-Nov	Capricornus
Mid-Nov to mid-Dec	Aquarius
Late December	Pisces

Jupiter

The giant planet kicks off 2018 in the morning sky; by mid-March, it's rising before midnight. Jupiter reaches opposition on **9 May**, and is visible in the evening sky until early November. All this time, the king of the planets lies in Libra. When it reappears just before sunrise, in late December, you'll find Jupiter in Ophiuchus.

Saturn

The ringed planet is skulking low in the sky, in Sagittarius. Saturn is prominent in the morning sky at the start of 2018 and is visible all night when it reaches opposition on **27 June**. Saturn slips into the evening twilight at the very end of the year.

Uranus
Just perceptible to the naked eye, Uranus is visible in the evening sky from January to March, lying in Pisces. In June, the seventh planet emerges in the dawn sky in Aries, where it remains for the rest of the year. Uranus is at opposition on **24 October**.

Neptune
The most distant planet lies in Aquarius all year, and is at opposition on **7 September**. Neptune can be seen – though only through binoculars or a telescope – in January and early February, and then from April until the end of the year.

SOLAR ECLIPSES

On **15 February**, people in Antarctica and the southern regions of South America will witness a partial eclipse of the Sun; it's not visible from the UK.

The southernmost regions of Australia and New Zealand are treated to a partial solar eclipse on **13 July**; not visible from the UK.

On **11 August**, a partial solar eclipse can be seen from northern Europe, north-east Canada and north-east Asia. People in the very north of the Scottish mainland, Orkney and Shetland will see a tiny chunk taken out of the Sun (see page 52).

ASTRONOMICAL DISTANCES

For objects in the Solar System, such as the planets, we can give their distances from the Earth in kilometres. But the distances are just too huge once we reach out to the stars. Even the nearest star (Proxima Centauri) lies 25 million million kilometres away.

So astronomers use a larger unit – the light year. This is the distance that light travels in one year, and it equals 9.46 million million kilometres.

Here are the distances to some familiar astronomical objects, in light years:

Proxima Centauri	4.2
Betelgeuse	640
Centre of the Milky Way	27,000
Andromeda Galaxy	2.5 million
Most distant galaxies seen by Hubble Space Telescope	13 billion

LUNAR ECLIPSES

A total lunar eclipse on **31 January** is visible from North America, Asia and Australasia, but not from the UK.

On **27 July**, a total eclipse of the Moon is visible from Africa, Europe and western Asia. As seen from Britain, the Moon rises totally eclipsed in the south-east around 9 pm, as a dim coppery globe directly above brilliant red Mars (see page 46).

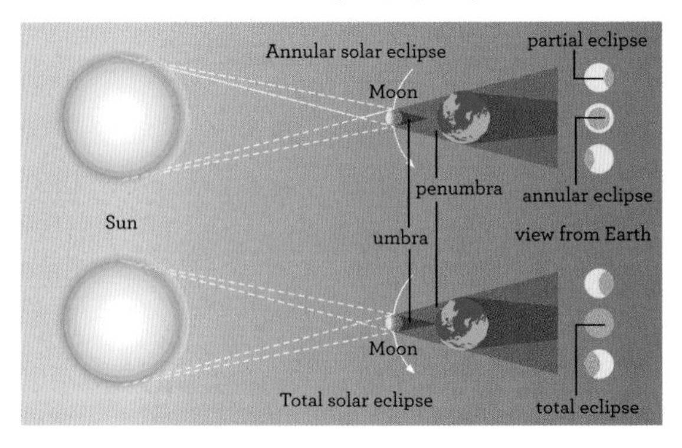

Where the dark central part (the umbra) of the Moon's shadow reaches the Earth, we see a total eclipse. People located within the penumbra see a partial eclipse. If the umbral shadow does not reach the Earth, we see an annular eclipse. This type of eclipse occurs when the Moon is at a distant point in its orbit and is not quite large enough to cover the whole of the Sun's disc.

Dates of maximum for selected meteor showers	
Meteor Shower	**Date of maximum**
Quadrantids	3/4 January
Lyrids	22/23 April
Eta Aquarids	5/6 May
Perseids	12/13 August
Orionids	21/22 October
Leonids	17/18 November
Geminids	13/14 December

METEOR SHOWERS

Shooting stars – or *meteors* – are tiny specks of interplanetary dust, burning up in the Earth's atmosphere. At certain times of year, the Earth passes through a stream of debris (usually left behind by a comet) and we see a *meteor shower*. The meteors appear to emanate from a point in the sky known as the *radiant*. Most showers are known by the constellation in which the radiant lies.

When watching meteors for a co-ordinated meteor programme, observers generally note the time, seeing conditions, cloud cover, their own location, the time and brightness of each meteor, and whether it was from the main meteor stream. It is also worth noting details of persistent afterglows (trains) and fireballs, and making counts of how many meteors appear in a given period.

There's also a slight chance of meteor showers on **8/9 October** and **6/7 December** this year, when the Earth runs into wayward debris streams (see October's and December's Special Events).

COMETS

Comets are small bodies in orbit about the Sun. Consisting of frozen gases and dust, they are often known as 'dirty snowballs'. When their orbits bring them close to the Sun, the ices evaporate and dramatic tails of gas and dust can sometimes be seen.

A number of comets move round the Sun in fairly small, elliptical orbits in periods of a few years; others have much longer periods. Most really brilliant comets have orbital periods of several thousands or even millions of years.

Binoculars and wide-field telescopes provide the best views of comet tails. Larger telescopes with a high magnification are necessary to observe fine detail in the gaseous head (*coma*). Most comets are discovered with professional instruments, but a few are still found by experienced amateur astronomers.

Use binoculars to track down Comet Giacobini-Zinner in August–September. The highlight of the year is Comet Wirtanen, so bright it's visible to the naked eye in November–December. And watch out in case a brilliant new comet puts in a surprise appearance!

ANGULAR SEPARATIONS

Astronomers measure the distance between objects, as we see them in the sky, by the angle between the objects in degrees (symbol °). From the horizon to the point above your head is 90 degrees. All around the horizon is 360 degrees.

You can use your hand, held at arm's length, as a rough guide to angular distances, as follows:

Width of index finger	1°
Width of clenched hand	10°
Thumb to little finger on outspread hand	20°

For smaller distances, astronomers divide the degree into 60 arcminutes (symbol '), and the arcminute into 60 arcseconds (symbol ").

Deep-sky objects are 'fuzzy patches' that lie outside the Solar System. They include star clusters, nebulae and galaxies. To observe the majority of deep-sky objects you will need binoculars or a telescope, but there are also some beautiful naked-eye objects, notably the Pleiades and the Orion Nebula.

The faintest object that an instrument can see is its *limiting magnitude*. The table gives a rough guide, for good seeing conditions, for a variety of small- to medium-sized telescopes.

Limiting magnitude for small to medium telescopes	
Aperture (mm)	**Limiting magnitude**
50	+11.2
60	+11.6
70	+11.9
80	+12.2
100	+12.7
125	+13.2
150	+13.6

We have provided a selection of recommended deep-sky targets, together with their magnitudes. Some are described in more detail in our monthly 'Object' features. Look on the appropriate month's map to find which constellations are on view, and then choose your objects using the list below. We have provided celestial coordinates for readers with detailed star maps or Go To telescopes. The suggested times of year for viewing are when the constellation is highest in the sky in the late evening.

RECOMMENDED DEEP-SKY OBJECTS

Andromeda autumn and early winter	
M31 (NGC 224) Andromeda Galaxy	3rd-magnitude spiral galaxy *RA 00h 42.7m Dec +41° 16'*
M32 (NGC 221)	8th-magnitude elliptical galaxy, a companion to M31 *RA 00h 42.7m Dec +40° 52'*
M110 (NGC 205)	8th-magnitude elliptical galaxy *RA 00h 40.4m Dec +41° 41'*
NGC 7662 Blue Snowball	8th-magnitude planetary nebula *RA 23h 25.9m Dec +42° 33'*
Aquarius late autumn and early winter	
M2 (NGC 7089)	6th-magnitude globular cluster *RA 21h 33.5m Dec -00° 49'*
M72 (NGC 6981)	9th-magnitude globular cluster *RA 20h 53.5m Dec -12° 32'*
NGC 7293 Helix Nebula	7th-magnitude planetary nebula *RA 22h 29.6m Dec -20° 48'*
NGC 7009 Saturn Nebula	8th-magnitude planetary nebula *RA 21h 04.2m Dec -11° 22'*

Aries early winter	
NGC 772	10th-magnitude spiral galaxy *RA 01h 59.3m Dec +19° 01'*
Auriga winter	
M36 (NGC 1960)	6th-magnitude open cluster *RA 05h 36.1m Dec +34° 08'*
M37 (NGC 2099)	6th-magnitude open cluster *RA 05h 52.4m Dec +32° 33'*
M38 (NGC 1912)	6th-magnitude open cluster *RA 05h 28.7m Dec +35° 50'*
Cancer late winter to early spring	
M44 (NGC 2632) Praesepe or Beehive	3rd-magnitude open cluster *RA 08h 40.1m Dec +19° 59'*
M67 (NGC 2682)	7th-magnitude open cluster *RA 08h 50.4m Dec +11° 49'*
Canes Venatici visible all year	
M3 (NGC 5272)	6th-magnitude globular cluster *RA 13h 42.2m Dec +28° 23'*

M51 (NGC 5194/5) Whirlpool Galaxy	8th-magnitude spiral galaxy *RA 13h 29.9m Dec +47° 12'*
M63 (NGC 5055)	9th-magnitude spiral galaxy *RA 13h 15.8m Dec +42° 02'*
M94 (NGC 4736)	8th-magnitude spiral galaxy *RA 12h 50.9m Dec +41° 07'*
M106 (NGC 4258)	8th-magnitude spiral galaxy *RA 12h 19.0m Dec +47° 18'*

Canis Major late winter

M41 (NGC 2287)	4th-magnitude open cluster *RA 06h 47.0m Dec -20° 44'*

Capricornus late summer and early autumn

M30 (NGC 7099)	7th-magnitude globular cluster *RA 21h 40.4m Dec -23° 11'*

Cassiopeia visible all year

M52 (NGC 7654)	6th-magnitude open cluster *RA 23h 24.2m Dec +61° 35'*
M103 (NGC 581)	7th-magnitude open cluster *RA 01h 33.2m Dec +60° 42'*
NGC 225	7th-magnitude open cluster *RA 00h 43.4m Dec +61° 47'*
NGC 457	6th-magnitude open cluster *RA 01h 19.1m Dec +58° 20'*
NGC 663	Good binocular open cluster *RA 01h 46.0m Dec +61° 15'*

Cepheus visible all year

Delta Cephei	Variable star, varying between +3.5 and +4.4 with a period of 5.37 days. It has a magnitude +6.3 companion and they make an attractive pair for small telescopes or binoculars.

Cetus late autumn

Mira (omicron Ceti)	Irregular variable star with a period of roughly 330 days and a range between +2.0 and +10.1.
M77 (NGC 1068)	9th-magnitude spiral galaxy *RA 02h 42.7m Dec -00° 01'*

Coma Berenices spring

M53 (NGC 5024)	8th-magnitude globular cluster *RA 13h 12.9m Dec +18° 10'*
M64 (NGC 4286) Black Eye Galaxy	8th-magnitude spiral galaxy with a prominent dust lane that is visible in larger telescopes. *RA 12h 56.7m Dec +21° 41'*
M85 (NGC 4382)	9th-magnitude elliptical galaxy *RA 12h 25.4m Dec +18° 11'*
M88 (NGC 4501)	10th-magnitude spiral galaxy *RA 12h 32.0m Dec.+14° 25'*
M91 (NGC 4548)	10th-magnitude spiral galaxy *RA 12h 35.4m Dec +14° 30'*
M98 (NGC 4192)	10th-magnitude spiral galaxy *RA 12h 13.8m Dec +14° 54'*
M99 (NGC 4254)	10th-magnitude spiral galaxy *RA 12h 18.8m Dec +14° 25'*
M100 (NGC 4321)	9th-magnitude spiral galaxy *RA 12h 22.9m Dec +15° 49'*
NGC 4565	10th-magnitude spiral galaxy *RA 12h 36.3m Dec +25° 59'*

Cygnus late summer and autumn

Cygnus Rift	Dark cloud just south of Deneb that appears to split the Milky Way in two.
NGC 7000 North America Nebula	A bright nebula against the background of the Milky Way, visible with binoculars under dark skies. *RA 20h 58.8m Dec +44° 20'*
NGC 6992 Veil Nebula (part)	Supernova remnant, visible with binoculars under dark skies. *RA 20h 56.8m Dec +31 28'*
M29 (NGC 6913)	7th-magnitude open cluster *RA 20h 23.9m Dec +36° 32'*
M39 (NGC 7092)	Large 5th-magnitude open cluster *RA 21h 32.2m Dec +48° 26'*
NGC 6826 Blinking Planetary	9th-magnitude planetary nebula *RA 19 44.8m Dec +50° 31'*

Delphinus late summer

NGC 6934	9th-magnitude globular cluster *RA 20h 34.2m Dec +07° 24'*

Draco midsummer

NGC 6543	9th-magnitude planetary nebula *RA 17h 58.6m Dec +66° 38'*

Gemini winter

M35 (NGC 2168)	5th-magnitude open cluster *RA 06h 08.9m Dec +24° 20'*
NGC 2392 Eskimo Nebula	8–10th-magnitude planetary nebula *RA 07h 29.2m Dec +20° 55'*

Hercules early summer

M13 (NGC 6205)	6th-magnitude globular cluster *RA 16h 41.7m Dec +36° 28'*
M92 (NGC 6341)	6th-magnitude globular cluster *RA 17h 17.1m Dec +43° 08'*
NGC 6210	9th-magnitude planetary nebula *RA 16h 44.5m Dec +23 49'*

Hydra early spring	
M48 (NGC 2548)	6th-magnitude open cluster *RA 08h 13.8m Dec -05° 48'*
M68 (NGC 4590)	8th-magnitude globular cluster *RA 12h 39.5m Dec -26° 45'*
M83 (NGC 5236)	8th-magnitude spiral galaxy *RA 13h 37.0m Dec -29° 52'*
NGC 3242 Ghost of Jupiter	9th-magnitude planetary nebula *RA 10h 24.8m Dec -18° 38'9*

Leo spring	
M65 (NGC 3623)	9th-magnitude spiral galaxy *RA 11h 18.9m Dec +13° 05'*
M66 (NGC 3627)	9th-magnitude spiral galaxy *RA 11h 20.2m Dec +12° 59'*
M95 (NGC 3351)	10th-magnitude spiral galaxy *RA 10h 44.0m Dec +11° 42'*
M96 (NGC 3368)	9th-magnitude spiral galaxy *RA 10h 46.8m Dec +11° 49'*
M105 (NGC 3379)	9th-magnitude elliptical galaxy *RA 10h 47.8m Dec +12° 35'*

Lepus winter	
M79 (NGC 1904)	8th-magnitude globular cluster *RA 05h 24.5m Dec -24° 33'*

Lyra spring	
M56 (NGC 6779)	8th-magnitude globular cluster *RA 19h 16.6m Dec +30° 11'*
M57 (NGC 6720) Ring Nebula	9th-magnitude planetary nebula *RA 18h 53.6m Dec +33° 02'*

Monoceros winter	
M50 (NGC 2323)	6th-magnitude open cluster *RA 07h 03.2m Dec -08° 20'*
NGC 2244	Open cluster surrounded by the faint Rosette Nebula, NGC 2237. Visible in binoculars. *RA 06h 32.4m Dec +04° 52'*

Ophiuchus summer	
M9 (NGC 6333)	8th-magnitude globular cluster *RA 17h 19.2m Dec -18° 31'*
M10 (NGC 6254)	7th-magnitude globular cluster *RA 16h 57.1m Dec -04° 06'*
M12 (NCG 6218)	7th-magnitude globular cluster *RA 16h 47.2m Dec -01° 57'*
M14 (NGC 6402)	8th-magnitude globular cluster *RA 17h 37.6m Dec -03° 15'*
M19 (NGC 6273)	7th-magnitude globular cluster *RA 17h 02.6m Dec -26° 16'*
M62 (NGC 6266)	7th-magnitude globular cluster *RA 17h 01.2m Dec -30° 07'*
M107 (NGC 6171)	8th-magnitude globular cluster *RA 16h 32.5m Dec -13° 03'*

Orion winter	
M42 (NGC 1976) Orion Nebula	4th-magnitude nebula *RA 05h 35.4m Dec -05° 27'*
M43 (NGC 1982)	5th-magnitude nebula *RA 05h 35.6m Dec -05° 16'*
M78 (NGC 2068)	8th-magnitude nebula *RA 05h 46.7m Dec +00° 03'*

Pegasus autumn	
M15 (NGC 7078)	6th-magnitude globular cluster *RA 21h 30.0m Dec +12° 10'*

Perseus autumn to winter	
M34 (NGC 1039)	5th-magnitude open cluster *RA 02h 42.0m Dec +42° 47'*
M76 (NGC 650/1) Little Dumbbell	11th-magnitude planetary nebula *RA 01h 42.4m Dec +51° 34'*
NGC 869/884 Double Cluster	Pair of open star clusters *RA 02h 19.0m Dec +57° 09'* *RA 02h 22.4m Dec +57° 07'*

Pisces autumn	
M74 (NGC 628)	9th-magnitude spiral galaxy *RA 01h 36.7m Dec +15° 47'*

Puppis late winter	
M46 (NGC 2437)	6th-magnitude open cluster *RA 07h 41.8m Dec -14° 49'*
M47 (NGC 2422)	4th-magnitude open cluster *RA 07h 36.6m Dec -14° 30'*
M93 (NGC 2447)	6th-magnitude open cluster *RA 07h 44.6m Dec -23° 52'*

Sagitta late summer	
M71 (NGC 6838)	8th-magnitude globular cluster *RA 19h 53.8m Dec +18° 47'*

Sagittarius summer	
M8 (NGC 6523) Lagoon Nebula	6th-magnitude nebula *RA 18h 03.8m Dec -24° 23'*
M17 (NGC 6618) Omega Nebula	6th-magnitude nebula *RA 18h 20.8m Dec -16° 11'*
M18 (NGC 6613)	7th-magnitude open cluster *RA 18h 19.9m Dec -17 08'*
M20 (NGC 6514) Trifid Nebula	9th-magnitude nebula *RA 18h 02.3m Dec -23° 02'*

M21 (NGC 6531)	6th-magnitude open cluster *RA 18h 04.6m Dec -22° 30′*
M22 (NGC 6656)	5th-magnitude globular cluster *RA 18h 36.4m Dec -23° 54′*
M23 (NGC 6494)	5th-magnitude open cluster *RA 17h 56.8m Dec -19° 01′*
M24 (NGC 6603)	5th-magnitude open cluster *RA 18h 16.9m Dec -18° 29′*
M25 (IC 4725)	5th-magnitude open cluster *RA 18h 31.6m Dec -19° 15′*
M28 (NGC 6626)	7th-magnitude globular cluster *RA 18h 24.5m Dec -24° 52′*
M54 (NGC 6715)	8th-magnitude globular cluster *RA 18h 55.1m Dec -30° 29′*
M55 (NGC 6809)	7th-magnitude globular cluster *RA 19h 40.0m Dec -30° 58′*
M69 (NGC 6637)	8th-magnitude globular cluster *RA 18h 31.4m Dec -32° 21′*
M70 (NGC 6681)	8th-magnitude globular cluster *RA 18h 43.2m Dec -32° 18′*
M75 (NGC 6864)	9th-magnitude globular cluster *RA 20h 06.1m Dec -21° 55′*

Scorpius (northern part) midsummer

M4 (NGC 6121)	6th-magnitude globular cluster *RA 16h 23.6m Dec -26° 32′*
M7 (NGC 6475)	3rd-magnitude open cluster *RA 17h 53.9m Dec -34° 49′*
M80 (NGC 6093)	7th-magnitude globular cluster *RA 16h 17.0m Dec -22° 59′*

Scutum mid to late summer

M11 (NGC 6705) Wild Duck Cluster	6th-magnitude open cluster *RA 18h 51.1m Dec -06° 16′*
M26 (NGC 6694)	8th-magnitude open cluster *RA 18h 45.2m Dec -09° 24′*

Serpens summer

M5 (NGC 5904)	6th-magnitude globular cluster *RA 15h 18.6m Dec +02° 05′*
M16 (NGC 6611)	6th-magnitude open cluster, surrounded by the Eagle Nebula. *RA 18h 18.8m Dec -13° 47′*

Taurus winter

M1 (NGC 1952) Crab Nebula	8th-magnitude supernova remnant *RA 05h 34.5m Dec +22° 00′*
M45 Pleiades	1st-magnitude open cluster, an excellent binocular object. *RA 03h 47.0m Dec +24° 07′*

Triangulum autumn

M33 (NGC 598)	6th-magnitude spiral galaxy *RA 01h 33.9m Dec +30° 39′*

Ursa Major all year

M81 (NGC 3031)	7th-magnitude spiral galaxy *RA 09h 55.6m Dec +69° 04′*
M82 (NGC 3034)	8th-magnitude starburst galaxy *RA 09h 55.8m Dec +69° 41′*
M97 (NGC 3587) Owl Nebula	12th-magnitude planetary nebula *RA 11h 14.8m Dec +55° 01′*
M101 (NGC 5457)	8th-magnitude spiral galaxy *RA 14h 03.2m Dec +54° 21′*
M108 (NGC 3556)	10th-magnitude spiral galaxy *RA 11h 11.5m Dec +55° 40′*
M109 (NGC 3992)	10th-magnitude spiral galaxy *RA 11h 57.6m Dec +53° 23′*

Virgo spring

M49 (NGC 4472)	8th-magnitude elliptical galaxy *RA 12h 29.8m Dec +08° 00′*
M58 (NGC 4579)	10th-magnitude spiral galaxy *RA 12h 37.7m Dec +11° 49′*
M59 (NGC 4621)	10th-magnitude elliptical galaxy *RA 12h 42.0m Dec +11° 39′*
M60 (NGC 4649)	9th-magnitude elliptical galaxy *RA 12h 43.7m Dec +11° 33′*
M61 (NGC 4303)	10th-magnitude spiral galaxy *RA 12h 21.9m Dec +04° 28′*
M84 (NGC 4374)	9th-magnitude elliptical galaxy *RA 12h 25.1m Dec +12° 53′*
M86 (NGC 4406)	9th-magnitude elliptical galaxy *RA 12h 26.2m Dec +12° 57′*
M87 (NGC 4486)	9th-magnitude elliptical galaxy *RA 12h 30.8m Dec +12° 24′*
M89 (NGC 4552)	10th-magnitude elliptical galaxy *RA 12h 35.7m Dec +12° 33′*
M90 (NGC 4569)	9th-magnitude spiral galaxy *RA 12h 36.8m Dec +13° 10′*
M104 (NGC 4594) Sombrero Galaxy	Almost edge-on 8th-magnitude spiral galaxy. *RA 12h 40.0m Dec -11° 37′*

Vulpecula late summer and autumn

M27 (NGC 6853) Dumbbell Nebula	8th-magnitude planetary nebula *RA 19h 59.6m Dec +22° 43′*

BINOCULARS OR TELESCOPE?

BY ROBIN SCAGELL

Mention to people that you are interested in astronomy, and the first question they ask is often, 'Have you got a telescope?' Indeed, every budding astronomer yearns for a telescope, and the bigger the better. But then reality kicks in. Can you afford one? What sort should it be? What will you see with it? And, in many cases, where will you keep it?

However, there's an alternative: binoculars. There's a strong argument for recommending that the first instrument you should buy is a reasonable pair of binoculars. Not only are they comparatively cheap, they will help you learn the sky, are more portable than a telescope, and have uses other than for astronomy. As an amateur astronomer with a range of telescopes up to 300 mm aperture, I would not be without my binoculars. So what are the merits of binoculars – and will they really satisfy that need to see the wonders of the heavens, or would you be better off going for a telescope anyway?

WHAT THEY DO

Optically speaking, binoculars are basically two low-magnification refracting telescopes side by side. Their specification, such as 10 × 50, gives the basic details. In this case, 10 is the magnification, hence '10 ×' standing for 'ten times', though in speech one always says 'ten by fifty' rather than 'ten times fifty'. The diameter of the objective lenses at the front (known to astronomers as the aperture) is 50 mm.

The aperture determines the size and weight of the instrument, so if you find 50 mm binoculars too bulky for you, you will have to go down to 40 mm or even 30 mm models. It's the eyepiece rather than the aperture that gives the magnification, though in general if you want more magnification, you need larger objectives to keep a bright image. The magnification of binoculars is usually fixed, typically 7 or 8 for small and

With binoculars you can be observing within seconds if a clear spell presents itself. Observing with both eyes, rather than one as with a telescope, gives a more natural view and allows you to see maximum detail.

medium binoculars, up to 20 or 25 for very large binoculars. The higher the magnification, usually the smaller the actual field of view.

For astronomy, the standard 10 × 50 model is a good all-rounder, offering a reasonable magnification without being too heavy. You can get 7 × 50 binoculars, which in theory give a brighter view, but beware! The pupils of our eyes simply don't open wide enough to make use of all the light once we reach middle age, so you might not appreciate the advantage. At the other end of the scale, you can get very high magnifications, such as 100, being offered in 50 mm binoculars, usually at the high end of a zoom range. The ads may claim that they are 'ideal for astronomy', but the image at such a magnification will be so dim that you won't see anything, and they will be impossible to hold steady.

Telescopes have generally larger objectives and higher magnifications, but with astronomical telescopes you can change the eyepiece to give different magnifications. A small telescope will have an aperture or 60 or 70 mm, and its lowest magnification is likely to be around 25. Many amateur astronomers have telescopes in the size range 130 mm–200 mm.

So telescopes take over from binoculars in terms of magnification, with little overlap. One big difference, however, is that astronomical telescopes almost always give an upside-down view, because this uses the simplest system with the least glass to absorb light. So if you want a telescope for terrestrial as well as astronomical use, make sure that it will give an upright or erect view. This

Many leading telescope suppliers sell good quality but reasonably priced binoculars, retailing for £50 or less. The widely available Helios Solana range is provided in 8 × 40, 7 × 50, 10 × 50, 12 × 50 and 16 × 50 sizes.

facility is usually only available in the smaller refracting telescopes – the traditional type, with a lens at the top of the tube. Anything above about 120 mm is likely to be a reflecting telescope, using mirrors at the bottom of the tube to capture and focus the light.

On the face of it, you might think that telescopes have it all the way. They are bigger and magnify more. But as with binoculars, the more you magnify, the less of the sky you can see at any one time. In terms of looking at the sky, binoculars typically have an actual field of view of around five degrees, which is roughly the separation of any two adjacent bright stars in the well-known shape of the Plough, Ursa Major. By contrast, even at its lowest magnification, a telescope might have a field of view of a degree or so, which is a patch of sky about the size of your index finger at arm's length.

The Moon, photographed in twilight by pointing a digital camera into the eyepiece of 10 × 50 binoculars. The visual view is very similar, allowing you to study the Moon's major features.

VIEWING WITH BINOCULARS

Binoculars come into their own when you are simply stargazing, as they reveal stars perhaps 50 times fainter than you can see with the naked eye alone. In good skies they are ideal for scanning along the Milky Way, and will show you star clusters and nebulae that are otherwise beyond your perception. Such objects as the Orion Nebula and the Pleiades star cluster are easy meat, while the Double Cluster in Perseus is a truly glorious sight. Nebulae such as the Omega Nebula, M17, spring into view. And if there is a decent comet around, binoculars are ideal for spotting it. It's even possible to carry out observations useful to science, such as by monitoring stars that vary in brightness.

Even galaxies are within the reach of binoculars. I have seen the Andromeda Galaxy, M31, from the centre of London with binoculars. Admittedly it was not spectacular, but it wasn't hard to find. The trick is to get away from immediate lights, such as in a park. In average out-of-town skies, even with standard 10 × 50 binoculars I can see much fainter galaxies, such as M81 and M82, and even a few in the distant Virgo Cluster. But a little more magnification does help when it comes to the smaller and fainter objects, and you can get 15 × 70 binoculars, which excel at finding the more elusive objects, at very reasonable prices though they are more cumbersome for everyday use.

The Moon is transformed from the familiar globe with patches of light and dark into a world of craters and mountains. But what you won't see with binoculars is any detail on the planets. Venus when close to Earth is large enough to show its crescent phase, while Jupiter is clearly larger than a star and is accompanied by up to four of its brightest moons. Saturn is slightly elongated, but with hand on heart you couldn't really say that you can see that it has rings. All the other planets are too small to show even a disc, though you can at least see Uranus and Neptune, which are beyond naked-eye visibility.

No, for these and many other objects there is nothing for it but to get a telescope.

A small refracting telescope – in this case an 80 mm refractor – will show some details on the planets and can also reveal many deep-sky objects that are out of reach of typical binoculars.

THE TELESCOPIC VIEW

As you'd expect, a vastly increased range of objects is visible with even a small telescope, of maybe 70–80 mm aperture. You can view the Moon as if flying over its surface, detail is visible on Jupiter and (when it is close) Mars. Those famous rings quite clearly girdle Saturn, and even Uranus and Neptune show tiny discs.

Some of the binocular highlights are now rather too large to be seen at their best. You may see only part of the Pleiades, and perhaps only one half of the Double Cluster. But to make up for that, you can now target many more star clusters, nebulae and galaxies. One word of warning – don't expect them to look like they do in photos, such as those in this book. No telescope is good enough to bring out the colours of the gases that make the Orion Nebula or the Helix Nebula such favourites, for example. The limitation is your eye's poor colour response in low light.

Given good skies, literally hundreds of galaxies in the Virgo Cluster are within your reach, though they will be what amateur astronomers refer to as 'faint fuzzies'. The thrill lies in finding them, rather than seeing a spectacular sight. Telescopes of 300 mm aperture and larger and dark skies are needed to reveal the arms of even the brightest spiral galaxies.

SO WHICH IS BEST?

As we've seen, there are pros and cons with both. For beginners, the choice may depend on lifestyle. In a city centre, a telescope will probably be more use than binoculars as the main things you can observe will be the Moon and planets. But out in the country, binoculars will give you glorious views of star fields and bright nebulae. Portability and size can also play a part. Even a small telescope takes up space, and binoculars are much easier to pack for that holiday flight.

But no matter how good your binoculars, and whatever your circumstances, if you are keen on observing you will eventually want a telescope. You may progress from a small to a larger one, buying and selling as time goes on. But you will keep your trusty binoculars. So don't hesitate to buy them – they will probably last you a lifetime of observing.

The wide field of view of binoculars makes them ideal for observing comets. From the dark skies of Arizona, Jeremy Perez drew this montage view of Comet 2004 M4 Swan through 10 × 50 binoculars. The globular cluster M13 is visible near the end of the comet's tail.

COURTESY OF CPRE/LUC

Our view of the stars – a source of infinite amazement for scientists, stargazers and the millions of us who seek out rural places to rest and recuperate – is obscured by light pollution. It's a sad fact that many people may never see the Milky Way, our own galaxy, because of the impact of artificial light.

LIGHT POLLUTION

Light pollution is a generic term referring to artificial light that shines where it is neither wanted nor needed. In broad terms, there are three types of light pollution:

- **Skyglow** – the pink or orange glow we see for miles around towns and cities, spreading deep into the countryside, caused by a scattering of artificial light by airborne dust and water droplets.
- **Glare** – the uncomfortable brightness of a light source.
- **Light intrusion** – light spilling beyond the boundary of the property on which a light is located, sometimes shining through windows and curtains.

The Campaign to Protect Rural England (CPRE) has long fought for the protection and improvement of dark skies, and against the spread of unnecessary artificial light. CPRE commissioned LUC to create new maps of Great Britain's light pollution and dark skies to give an accurate picture of how much light is spilling up into the night sky and show where urgent action is needed. CPRE also sought to find where the darkest skies are, so that they can be protected and improved.

MAPPING

The new maps are based on data gathered by the National Oceanographic and Atmospheric Administration (NOAA) in America, using the Suomi NPP weather satellite. One of the instruments on board the satellite is the Visible Infrared Imaging Radiometer Suite (VIIRS), which captures visible and infrared imagery to monitor and measure processes on Earth, including the amount of light spilling up into the night sky. This light is captured by a day/night band sensor.

The mapping used data gathered in September 2015, and is made up of a composite of nightly images taken that month as the satellite passes over the UK at 1.30am.

The data was split into nine categories to distinguish between different light levels. Colours were assigned to each category, ranging from darkest to brightest, as shown in the chart below. The maps

Colour bandings to show levels of brightness

Categories	Brightness values (in nw/cm²/sr)*
Colour band 1 (darkest)	<0.25
Colour band 2	0.25–0.5
Colour band 3	0.5–1
Colour band 4	1–2
Colour band 5	2–4
Colour band 6	4–8
Colour band 7	8–16
Colour band 8	16–32
Colour band 9 (brightest)	>32

**The brightness values are measured in nanowatts/cm²/steradian (nw/cm²/sr). In simple terms, this calculates how the satellite instruments measure the light on the ground, taking account of the distance between the two.*

are divided into pixels, 400 metres × 400 metres, to show the amount of light shining up into the night sky from that area. This is measured by the satellite in nanowatts, which is then used to create a measure of night-time brightness.

The nine colour bands were applied to a national map of Great Britain (see the following pages), which clearly identifies the main concentrations of night-time lights, creating light pollution that spills up into the sky.

The highest levels of light pollution are around towns and cities, with the highest densities around London, Leeds, Manchester, Liverpool, Birmingham and Newcastle. Heavily lit transport infrastructure, such as major roads, ports and airports, also show up clearly on the map. The national map also shows that there are many areas that have very little light pollution, where people can expect to see a truly dark night sky.

The results show that only 21.7 per cent of England has pristine night skies, completely free from light pollution (see the chart below). This compares with almost 57 per cent of Wales and 77 per cent of Scotland. When the two darkest categories are combined, 49 per cent of England can be considered dark, compared with almost 75 per cent in Wales and 87.5 per cent in Scotland. There are noticeably higher levels of light pollution in England in all the categories, compared with Wales and Scotland. The amount of the most severe light pollution is five times higher in England than in Scotland and six times higher than in Wales.

The different levels of light pollution are linked to the varying population densities of the three countries: where there are higher population densities, there are higher levels of light pollution. For example, the Welsh Valleys are clearly shown by the fingers of light pollution spreading north from Newport, Cardiff, Bridgend and Swansea. In Scotland, the main populated areas stretching from Edinburgh to Glasgow show almost unbroken levels of light pollution, creeping out from the cities and towns to blur any distinction between urban and rural areas.

Light levels in England, Wales and Scotland

Categories	England	Wales	Scotland	GB
Colour band 1 (darkest)	21.7%	56.9%	76.8%	46.2%
Colour band 2	27.3%	18.0%	10.7%	20.1%
Colour band 3	19.1%	9.3%	4.6%	12.6%
Colour band 4	11.0%	5.8%	2.8%	7.3%
Colour band 5	6.8%	3.8%	1.7%	4.6%
Colour band 6	5.0%	2.9%	1.2%	3.3%
Colour band 7	4.3%	2.1%	1.0%	2.8%
Colour band 8	3.2%	1.0%	0.9%	2.1%
Colour band 9 (brightest)	1.6%	0.2%	0.3%	1.0%

Adapted from Night Blight: Mapping England's light pollution and dark skies *CPRE (2016), with kind permission from the Campaign to Protect Rural England. To see the full report and dedicated website, go to http://nightblight.cpre.org.uk/*

MAP OF BRITAIN'S LIGHT POLLUTION AND DARK SKIES

COURTESY OF CPRE/LUC

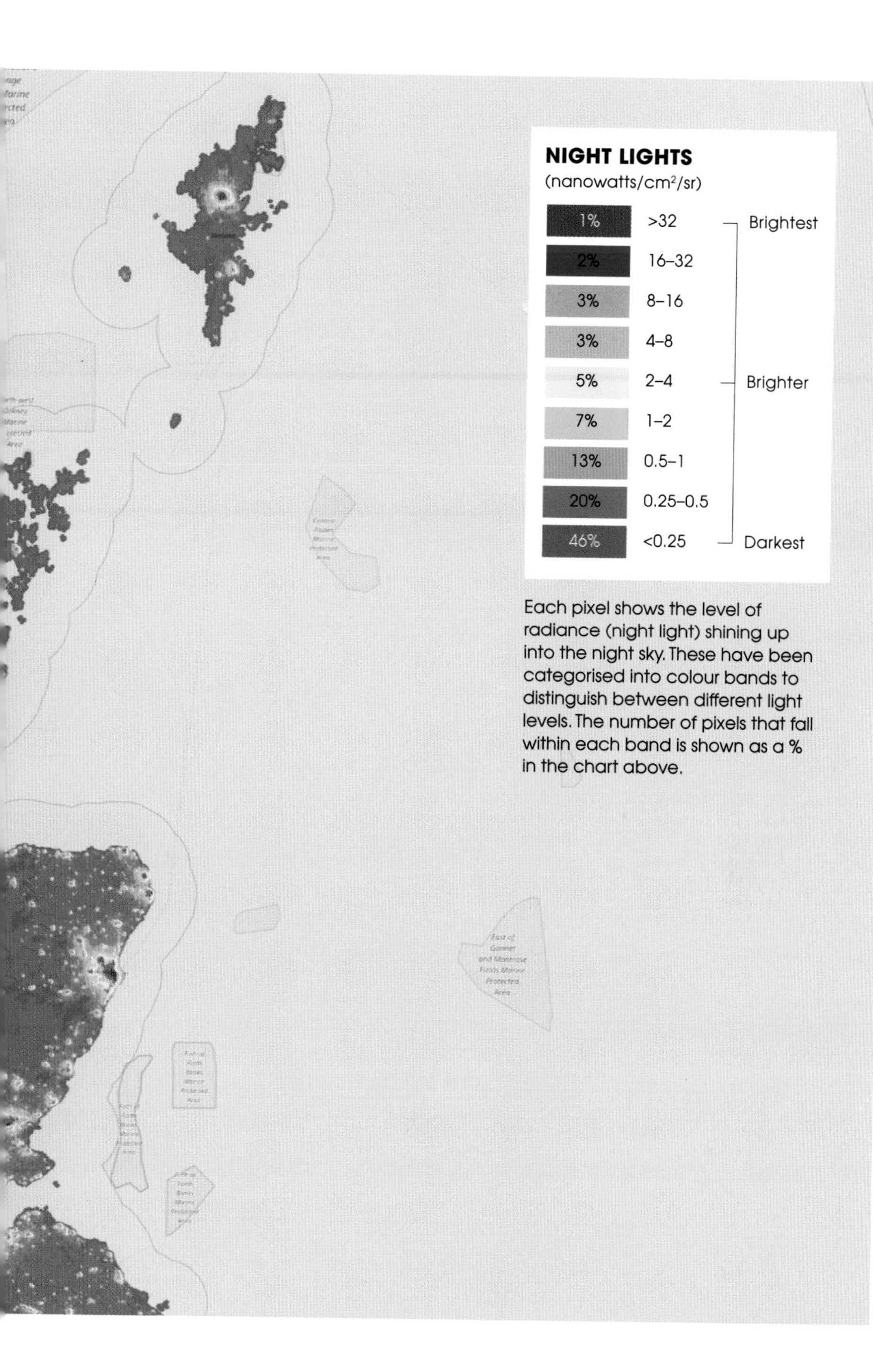
NIGHT LIGHTS
(nanowatts/cm²/sr)
1% >32 Brightest
2% 16–32
3% 8–16
3% 4–8
5% 2–4 Brighter
7% 1–2
13% 0.5–1
20% 0.25–0.5
46% <0.25 Darkest
Each pixel shows the level of radiance (night light) shining up into the night sky. These have been categorised into colour bands to distinguish between different light levels. The number of pixels that fall within each band is shown as a % in the chart above.
East of Gannet and Montrose Fields Marine Protected Area

Londonderry/
Derry
Antrim Coast & Glens AONB
Sperrins AONB
Northern Ireland
Belfast
Lisburn
Strangford & Lecale AONB
Armagh
Newry
Mourne & Slieve Croob AONB
Isle of Man
Dublin
Galway
Limerick
Waterford
Cork

Brugge
Gent
Dunkerque
Lille
Mons
Zeeland

THE AUTHORS

Heather Couper and **Nigel Henbest** – both Fellows of the Royal Astronomical Society – are internationally recognised writers and broadcasters on astronomy and space. As well as writing more than 40 books and 1000 articles, they founded an independent TV production company specialising in factual programming.

Heather is a past President of both the British Astronomical Association and the Society for Popular Astronomy. She is a Fellow of the Institute of Physics and a former Millennium Commissioner, for which she was awarded the CBE in 2007.

After researching at Cambridge, Nigel became a consultant to both *New Scientist* magazine and the Royal Greenwich Observatory, and edited the *Journal of the British Astronomical Association*. He is a future astronaut with Virgin Galactic.

ACKNOWLEDGEMENTS

PHOTOGRAPHS

Front cover: Damian Peach: Comet Lovejoy C/2012 Q2.

Galaxy Picture Library: John Bell 15; Andrew Davies 75; Optical Vision Ltd 87; Damian Peach 4, 39, 45, 57, 63; Jeremy Perez 89; Robin Scagell 86, 88 (top and bottom); Mary Spicer 69; Nik Symanek 27; Sara Wager 1, 2–3, 9, 33, 51

layritten/123RF.com: 10, 16, 22, 28, 34, 40, 46, 52, 58, 64, 60, 76

NASA: JPL/University of Arizona 11; NSS-DCA 29; JPL-Caltech 35, 65; Johns Hopkins University Applied Physics Laboratory/ Carnegie Institution of Washington 71

ARTWORKS

Star maps: Will Tirion/Philip's with extra annotation by Philip's

Planet event charts: Chris Bell using Starry Night 7

Pages 90–95: Adapted from *Night Blight: Mapping England's light pollution and dark skies* CPRE (2016), with kind permission from the Campaign to Protect Rural England. To see the full report and dedicated website, go to http://nightblight.cpre.org.uk/

Maps © OpenStreetMap contributors, Earth Observation Group, NOAA National Geophysical Data Center. Developed by CPRE and LUC.